ADVANCES IN BLACK HOLES RESEARCH

SPACE SCIENCE, EXPLORATION AND POLICIES

Additional books in this series can be found on Nova's website
under the Series tab.

Additional E-books in this series can be found on Nova's website
under the E-book tab.

SPACE SCIENCE, EXPLORATION AND POLICIES

ADVANCES IN BLACK HOLES RESEARCH

ABRAHAM BARTON
EDITOR

nova
publishers
New York

LIBRARY OF CONGRESS CATALOGING-IN-PUBLICATION DATA

Advances in black holes research / editor, Abraham Barton.
 pages cm. -- (Space science, exploration, and policies)
 Includes bibliographical references and index.
 ISBN 978-1-63463-168-6 (hardcover)
 1. Black holes (Astronomy) 2. Cosmology. 3. Gravitational fields. I. Barton, Abraham, 1969-editor.
 QB843.B55A33 2014
 523.8'875--dc23
 2014037732

Published by Nova Science Publishers, Inc. † New York

CONTENTS

PREFACE

The semi-classical description of black holes, as it was originally introduced by Hawking and Bekenstein in the early seventies, where classical solutions of the Einstein equations are coupled to quantum matter fields, opened a window with a glance on the quantum aspects of gravity. This book discusses this semi-classical approach to quantum black holes. It also discuses the philosophical issues about black holes; the Randall-Sundrum II model; the gravitational collapse in alternative theories of gravity; observational limits on modern extended gravity models; and generalized Brans-Dicke models from Kaluza-Klein reductions.

Semi-classical description of BH, as it was originally introduced by Hawking and Bekenstein in the early seventies, where classical solutions of the Einstein equations are coupled to quantum matter fields, opened for the first time a window with a glance on the quantum aspects of gravity. The surprising properties showed by semi-classical description of black holes (BHs) called for a full quantum description for such objects. In particular, the understanding of BH entropy in terms of micro-states, as well as the behavior during the final phase of evaporation, cannot be properly described in semi-classical terms.

Quantum gravity has a long story of doomed attempts to cure the theory from non-renormalizability and quantum anomalies. In the eighties Green and Schwarz brilliantly solved these problems in the framework of $SO(32)$ or $E_8 \times E_8$ super-symmetric quantum string theories. Up to now, string theory is the best candidate for a grand unified theory including gravity at the quantum level in a consistent way. Accepting that the building blocks of matter are one-dimensional extended objects, characterized by a length scale of order 10^{-33} *cm*, still the relation between fundamental strings and BHs remains to be determined. The exponential increase of string states degeneracy with the string excitation energy resembles the exponential increase of BH states with the increase of BH mass. This and other results suggest a correspondence between BHs and highly excited strings, or string balls. However, a more precise stringy formulation of BHs requires a non-perturbative formulation of the theory itself, including the interaction with higher dimensional objects, i.e., D-branes. So far, this approach provides the correct entropy counting BH micro-states only in a limited number of cases, but not in general.

In Chapter 1 the authors review a "phenomenological" approach taking into account the most fundamental feature of string theory or, more in general, of quantum gravity, whatever its origin, which is the existence of a minimal length in the space-time fabric. This length is generally identified with the Planck length, or the string length, but it could be also much longer down to the TeV region. A simple and effective way to keep track of the effects the minimal length in BH geometries is to solve the Einstein equations with an energy momentum tensor describing non point-like matter. The immediate consequence is the absence of any curvature singularity. Where textbook solutions of the Einstein equations lose any physical meaning because of infinite tidal forces, the authors' find a de Sitter vacuum core of high, but finite, energy density and pressure. An additional improvement regards the final stage of the BH evaporation leading to a vanishing Hawking temperature even in the neutral, non-rotating, case. In spite of the simplicity of this model we are able to describe the final stage of the BH evaporation, resulting in a cold remnant with a degenerate, extremal, horizon of radius of the order of the minimal length. In this chapter we shall describe only neutral, spherically symmetric, regular BHs although charged, rotating and higher dimensional BHs can be found in the literature.

Black holes are extremely relativistic objects. Physical processes around them occur in a regime where the gravitational field is extremely intense. Under such conditions, our representations of space, time, gravity, and thermodynamics are pushed to their limits. In such a situation philosophical issues naturally arise. In Chapter 2, the author reviews some philosophical questions related to black holes. In particular, the relevance of black holes for the metaphysical dispute between presentists and eternalists, the origin of the second law of thermodynamics and its relation to black holes, the problem of information, black holes and hypercomputing, the nature of determinisim, and the breakdown of predictability in black hole space-times. The author maintains that black hole physics can be used to illuminate some important problems in the border between science and philosophy, either epistemology or ontology.

Models postulating the existence of additional spacelike dimensions of macroscopic or even infinite size, while viewing our observable universe as merely a 3-brane living in a higher-dimensional bulk were a major breakthrough when proposed some 15 years ago. The most interesting among them both in terms of elegance of the setup and of the richness of the emerging phenomenology is the Randall-Sundrum II model where one infinite extra spacelike dimension is considered with an AdS topology, characterized by the warping effect caused by the presence of a negative cosmological constant in the bulk. A major drawback of this model is that despite numerous efforts no line element has been found so far that could describe a stable, regular, realistic black hole. Finding a smoothly behaved such solution supported by the presence of some more or less conventional fields either in the bulk and/or on the brane is the core of the black hole challenge. After a comprehensive presentation of the details of the model and the analysis of the significance and the utility of getting a specific analytic black hole solution, several (unsuccessful) analytic and numerical approaches to the problem developed over the years are presented with some discussion about their results. Chapter 3 closes with the latest numerical results that actually consists a major advancement in the effort to address the challenge, the presentation of the most recent analytic work trying (and unfortunately failing) to build a solution assuming the existence of unconventional scalar fields and some ideas about the routes forthcoming analytic approaches should explore.

General relativity has been extremely successful in describing gravitation in the solar system regime. However, when looking at the galactic, cosmological and infinitesimal scales of the universe, the model appears to meet a number of observational and theoretical problems. In order to retain the positive parts of the model while complementing the model with ramifications to better fit the observational evidence, modified theories of gravity have been proposed in Chapter 4. These are tested against data as well as against the theoretical issues that arise in general relativity itself.

In the present case the situation of gravitational collapse is investigated. The traditional general relativistic case is review with modifications for the so-called *f(R)* class of theories. Various examples of particular *f(R)* functions are explored. Other theories of gravity are then expanded upon with a look into their consequences for gravitational collapse. Finally the eventual fate of a collapsed system is reviewed.

Chapter 5 presents the ideas and some results (negative) on the experimental search for new physics from the Gauss-Bonnet and Randall-Sundrum gravities. The idea is to compare the anticipated experimental signals with the accuracy of modern gravitational experiments in our solar system and some cosmological tests. As a result, is it shown that the real search of the Gauss-Bonnet and Randall-Sundrum theories' predictions requires the increase of experimental accuracy.

In Chapter 6 the authors show that how a generalized Kaluza-Klein (KK) dimensional reduction of the higher dimensional n $\geq$ 4 Einstein-Hilbert action exists when more than one compactified coordinate introduced. The authors show that if they start by a metric with q numbers of commutative Killing vectors, the result is a *(n-q)* scalar-tensor theory in which a couple of scalar fields coupled non-minimally to the gravity. Explicitly the authors saw the emergence of a non-minimally coupled bi-scalar-tensor model for the higher dimensional classical action is natural. By starting from a curved space-time in *(D+p)* -dimensional *p*-static metric, the authors perform the successive *p*-time reduction, they obtain the Einstein gravity with a unique scalar field in *D*-dimensions.

In: Advances in Black Holes Research
Editor: Abraham Barton

ISBN: 978-1-63463-168-6
© 2015 Nova Science Publishers, Inc.

Chapter 1

SEMI-CLASSICAL APPROACH
TO QUANTUM BLACK HOLES

Euro Spallucci[*] *and Anais Smailagic*
Department of Theoretical Physics, University of Trieste, Trieste, Italy
Sezione INFN di Trieste, Trieste, Italy

Abstract

Semi-classical description of BH, as it was originally introduced by Hawking and Bekenstein in the early seventies, where classical solutions of the Einstein equations are coupled to quantum matter fields, opened for the first time a window with a glance on the quantum aspects of gravity. The surprising properties showed by semi-classical description of black holes (BHs) called for a full quantum description for such objects. In particular, the understanding of BH entropy in terms of micro-states, as well as the behavior during the final phase of evaporation, cannot be properly described in semi-classical terms.

Quantum gravity has a long story of doomed attempts to cure the theory from non-renormalizability and quantum anomalies. In the eighties Green and Schwarz brilliantly solved these problems in the framework of $SO(32)$ or $E_8 \times E_8$ super-symmetric quantum string theories. Up to now, string theory is the best candidate for a grand unified theory including gravity at the quantum level in a consistent way. Accepting that the building blocks of matter are one-dimensional extended objects, characterized by a length scale of order $10^{-33} cm$, still the relation between fundamental strings and BHs remains to be determined. The exponential increase of string states degeneracy with the string excitation energy resembles the exponential increase of BH states with the increase of BH mass. This and other results suggest a correspondence between BHs and highly excited strings, or string balls. However, a more precise stringy formulation of BHs requires a non-perturbative formulation of the theory itself, including the interaction with higher dimensional objects, i.e., D-branes. So far, this approach provides the correct entropy counting BH micro-states only in a limited number of cases, but not in general.

In this Chapter we would like to review a "phenomenological" approach taking into account the most fundamental feature of string theory or, more in general, of quantum gravity [1], whatever its origin, which is the existence of a minimal length in

---

[*]E-mail address: euro@ts.infn.it (Corresponding Author)

the space-time fabric [2]. This length is generally identified with the Planck length, or the string length, [3, 4] but it could be also much longer down to the TeV region. A simple and effective way to keep track of the effects the minimal length in BH geometries is to solve the Einstein equations with an energy momentum tensor describing non point-like matter. The immediate consequence is the absence of any curvature singularity. Where textbook solutions of the Einstein equations loose any physical meaning because of infinite tidal forces, we find a de Sitter vacuum core of high, but finite, energy density and pressure. An additional improvement regards the final stage of the BH evaporation leading to a vanishing Hawking temperature even in the neutral, non-rotating, case. In spite of the simplicity of this model we are able to describe the final stage of the BH evaporation, resulting in a cold remnant with a degenerate, extremal, horizon of radius of the order of the minimal length. In this chapter we shall describe only neutral, spherically symmetric, regular BHs although charged, rotating and higher dimensional BHs can be found in the literature [5, 6].

1. Introduction

The description of radiating BHs by Hawking [7] offered the first physically relevant "peep" on the mysteries of quantum gravity. After more than forty years of intensive research in this field (see [8, 9, 10] and [11] for a recent review with an extensive reference list) various aspects of the problem still remain to be properly explained. For example, a satisfactory description of the terminal stage of BH evaporation remains still to be understood. So far, the string theory seems to be the best candidate for self-consistent, ultraviolet completion of gravity at the Planck scale. On the other hand, following Bekenstein's idea, the BH entropy is formally identified with the area of the event horizon in Planck units. Thus, combining Hawking's definition of BH temperature with the Area Law gives a consistent thermodynamical description of semi-classical BHs dynamics. However, to give a physical ground to this interpretation one needs a proper identification of BH micro-states, i.e., a complete statistical interpretation of entropy. Beforehand one can say that the number of micro-states has to grow exponentially with the area, but the physical meaning of these micro-states is elusive in this semi-classical quantum framework. Contrary to the classical gas thermodynamics, where the entropy is a function of the volume enclosing the system, in the BH case entropy is a function of the area of the object indicating that the eventual BH micro-states should lie somewhere on the horizon surface instead of in the internal volume [1]

Interestingly enough, in string theory the degeneracy of excitation states also shows the same exponential growth. This suggests an identification among highly excited string states and BH micro-states. However, a more precise stringy formulation of Bhs requires a non-perturbative formulation of string theory itself, including the interaction with higher dimensional objects, i.e., D-branes. So far, this approach provides the correct entropy counting BH micro-states at least in a limited number of cases, but not yet in general.

In this Chapter we would like to review a "phenomenological" approach taking into account the most fundamental feature of string theory or, more in general, of quantum gravity, whatever its origin, which is the existence of a *minimal length* in the space-time

---

[1]This is a possible realization of the Holographic Principle which frequently pops up when dealing with quantum gravity [12, 13]. It seem to be a general property of self-gravitating quantum system that physical degrees of freedom are confined on the boundary enclosing the system, rather than in the bulk.

fabric [2]. This length is, so far, identified with the Planck length, or the string length, but nothing prevents it from being much longer, even down to the TeV region. A simple and effective way to keep track of the modifications of BH geometries, due to the presence of the minimal length, is to solve the Einstein equations with an energy momentum tensor describing non point-like matter.

At first glance,one could think of modifying the four dimensional Einstein action to incorporate minimal length effects. To solve the modified field equations can be quite complicated. This is the case, where minimal length is introduced in the Einstein theory through the, so-called, "star-product", i.e., the standard product between fields is replaced by a non-commutative product operation making even the simplest field theory non-local and impossible to solve. The only way to handle non-local field theories is in a truncated perturbative expansion suppressing non-locality and introducing spurious derivative inter-actions. In the resulting approximate theory, the effect of the minimal length as a natural short-distance cut-off is lost and paradoxically infrared divergences appear even in the mas-sive case and mix with the persisting ultraviolet divergences. A typical example of a "... cure killing the patient!".

The star-product approach, while formally correct is of little practical use. For exam-ple, BH perturbative solutions of "starred-product" Einstein equations, manifest the same pathological short distance behavior of the corresponding standard solutions, in spite of introducing a short-distance cut-off [14, 15].

We argued that an alternative approach is to implement the minimal length *only* in the matter source. The line of reasoning is the following. The metric field is a geometrical struc-ture defined over an underlying manifold and the curvature is a measure of the strength of the metric field. Thus, it is the response to the presence of a mass-energy distribution. The minimal length is an intrinsic property of the manifold itself, rather than a super-imposed geometrical structure. It affects gravity in a subtle, indirect way: it smears matter elimi-nating point-like objects as physical sources of the gravitational field. As a matter of fact, this idea goes hand-in-hand with the fundamental idea of string theory: "particles" are not matter-points, rather they are extended, one dimensional objects, whose length is of the order of the Planck length, or any other fundamental length scale. Following the above reasoning, we conclude that in General Relativity the effects of the minimal length can be taken into account by *keeping the standard form* of the Einstein tensor in the l.h.s. of the field equations and introducing a *modified energy-momentum tensor* as a source in the r.h.s.

At this point one may object that the textbook approach defines BHs as "matter-free" solutions of the field equations. Even in the case of the Reissner-Nordström BH, the energy momentum tensor *only* describes the electric field.

This way of introducing BHs is, at least, misleading and contradicts the fundamental ideas of General Relativity that the geometry of space-time is determined by the energy-momentum distribution.The *only* globally defined matter-free solution of the Einstein equa-tions is Minkowski space-time. Furthermore, solving "in vacuum" faces the problem of *a posteriori* determination of various integration constants. A crystal clear example of this difficulty is the Kerr solution, where integration constants are fixed by comparison with the geometry of a slowly rotating sphere, while everybody is aware that the rotating sphere is *not* the source of the the Kerr gravitation field!

Furthermore, the symmetry of the "vacuum" solution, has to be imposed *a priori*, since there is noting in the field equations that can do the job for you.

All the above mentioned ambiguities disappear once a proper matter source is introduced in the Einstein equations.

2. "Renormalizing" BHs: A Toy-Model

A well known example, in quantum field theory, of difficulties related to modeling elementary particles as structureless point like objects, is the appearance of ultraviolet infinities. When computing one-loop Feynman graphs, one finds infinite, unphysical, amplitudes for measurable processes. The simplest "cure" of the infinity disease is to introduce a suitable short-distance cut-off, which in coordinate-space is simply a "minimal length". Once divergent parts of the amplitudes are subtracted away, the (arbitrary) cut-off is replaced by sum physically meaningful quantity through a "re-normalization", i.e., re-parametrization, of the theory.

Following this philosophy, we propose to re-normalize the curvature singularity in a BH geometry in a similar fashion.

First, let us cut-off the singularity by introducing a minimal length into the line element.

Second, relate the minimal length to the radius of the smallest physically meaningful, *extremal* BH. This two-step procedure will be first applied to the simples case of Schwarzschild BH. In order to remove the curvature singularity in $r = 0$, we introduce the simplest kind of short-distance cutoff through the replacement

$$\frac{1}{r} \longrightarrow \frac{r^2}{r^3 + l_0^3} \tag{1}$$

where, l_0 is, for the moment, an arbitrary length scale. According with the framework one has in mind, l_0 can be thought of as the characteristic length scale of the underlying quantum theory of gravity (whatever it is), i.e., the Planck length, the string length, etc. In the technically much more involved approach of "asymptotically safe" quantum gravity, a similar "cutoff identification" was introduced in [16] for the same purpose [2], By skipping all the approach-dependent technicalities we write a regularized Schwarzschild metric as

$$ds^2 = -\left(1 - \frac{2G_N \mathcal{M}(r)}{r}\right) dt^2 + \left(1 - \frac{2G_N M(r)}{r}\right)^{-1} dr^2 + r^2 d\Omega^2 \tag{2}$$

where

$$\mathcal{M}(r) \equiv M \frac{r^3}{r^3 + l_0^3/2} \tag{3}$$

---

[2] Alternative choices of the cutoff function are

$$\frac{1}{r} \longrightarrow \frac{r^2}{r^3 + \omega G_N (r + \gamma G_N M)}$$

where, ω and γ are constants coming from non-perturbative renormalization group calculations [16]; or [17]

$$\frac{1}{r} \longrightarrow \frac{r^2}{r^3 + 2MG_N l_0^2}$$

From the equation (3) one sees the $\mathcal{M}(r) \longrightarrow M$ at large distance, i.e., $r >> l_0$, while in the opposite limit $M(r) \longrightarrow 2Mr^3/l_0^3$. As a consequence the metric approaches the standard form of the Schwarzschild line element at large distance, and the deSitter metric

$$ds^2 = -\left(1 - \frac{4G_N M}{l_0^3} r^2\right) dt^2 + \left(1 - \frac{4G_N M}{l_0^3} r^2\right)^{-1} dr^2 + r^2 d\Omega^2 \qquad (4)$$

at short distance, with an effective cosmological constant $\Lambda = 12G_N M/l_0^3$. The deSitter geometry is known to be curvature singularity-free. As a matter of fact, we have replaced a physically meaningless infinite curvature point with a central deSitter condensate, where the curvature can be very high but finite. The physical mechanism leading to the disappearance of the singularity is clear, as the deSitter vacuum exerts a *negative* pressure balancing the gravitation pull towards the center. Thus, close to the origin, collapsed matter is supported by the negative pressure of the deSitter vacuum and can attain an equilibrium configuration.

Step two, requires to identify the physical meaning of l_0 through an in depth study of the BH geometry.

The eventual horizons are obtained from the equation[3]:

$$M = \frac{r_H^3 + l_0^3/2}{2G_N r_H^2} \qquad (6)$$

The function (41) has a single minimum in

$$r_0 = l_0 , \qquad (7)$$
$$M_0 = \frac{3l_0}{4G_N} \qquad (8)$$

describing an *"extremal"* BH in the sense that for any $M > M_0$, the radius of the outer horizon, r_+, is larger than l_0.

The extremal BH can be understood as the thermodynamical equivalent of the "minimal volume" of a real gas V_0. As it known, the entropy of the gas is of the form $S = k_B \ln(V/V_0)$ leading to $S = 0$ for $V = V_0$. In the BH case, the role of the gas

---

[3]The radius of the inner and outer horizon can be obtained by solving the cubic algebraic equation

$$r_H^3 - 2MG_N r_H^2 + \frac{l_0^3}{2} = 0 \qquad (5)$$

For the sake of completeness, we give the exact solutions:

$$r_{<0} = \frac{2MG_N}{3}\left(1 - 2\cos\theta\right) ,$$
$$r_- = \frac{2MG_N}{3}\left(1 + 2\cos\left(\theta - \frac{\pi}{3}\right)\right) ,$$
$$r_+ = \frac{2MG_N}{3}\left(1 + 2\cos\left(\theta + \frac{\pi}{3}\right)\right) ,$$
$$\cos(3\theta) = -1 + 2\left(\frac{3l_0}{4MG_N}\right)^3$$

The first root is an unphysical negative solution. $r_\pm$ are the radii of the inner/outer horizons.

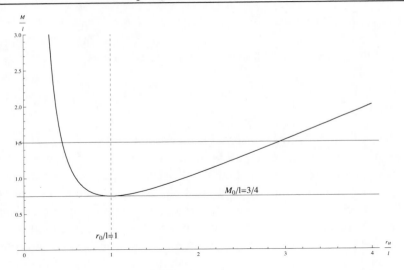

Figure 1. Plot of the function in equation (6).

with volume V_0 is played by the extremal BH which is expected to have zero entropy in agreement with the third law of thermodynamics.

A second, inner horizon r_-, exists for any non-extremal configuration (see Figure 1). r_+ and r_- merge into r_0 for $M \to M_0$. For $M < M_0$ no BH exists. Thus, l_0 has been promoted from an arbitrary parameter with length dimension, to radius of the horizon of the minimal size extremal BH[4].

Contrary to the case of the "bare" Schwarzschild BH, the renormalized metric admits and extremal configuration even in the absence of electric charge and angular momentum.

The existence of a de Sitter region at short distance, indicates the presence of a non-trivial energy-momentum tensor sourcing the renormalized metric (2). This energy-momentum tensor must approach a cosmological form at short-distance. The energy density for a spherically symmetric mass distribution is given by

$$\rho \equiv \frac{1}{4\pi r^2}\frac{d\mathcal{M}}{dr} = \frac{3M}{8\pi}\frac{l_0^3}{\left(r^3 + l_0^3/2\right)^2} \tag{9}$$

Let us remark that the invariant energy dentity is finite everywhere. In particular $\rho(0) = 3M/2\pi l_0^3$ and this is a necessary condition to avoid the appearance of a curvature singularity in the origin.

The complete energy momentum tensor encodes energy and pressure distributions of an anisotropic fluid [25] given by

$$T^\mu{}_\nu = -p_\theta\delta^\mu{}_\nu + (\rho + p_\theta)(-u^\mu u_\nu + l^\mu l_\nu) \tag{10}$$

where, $u^\mu = (1,0,0,0)$, $l^\mu = (0,1,0,0)$, and $p_\theta = \rho + (r/2)d\rho/dr$ follows from the energy-momentum tensor covariant divergence-free condition. p_θ is finite everywhere as

---

[4]If the smallest object can be produced is an extremal BH of size l_0 [19, 20, 21], there is no physical way to probe sub-Planckian distances [22, 23, 24].

well. Thus, we have a regular source leading to the everywhere finite curvature geometry described by the line element (2).

2.1. Thermodynamics

The thermodynamical description of BH starts with the computation of the Hawking temperature defined as the surface gravity of the Killing horizon over 4π:

$$T_H \equiv \frac{\kappa_H}{4\pi} = \frac{1}{\sqrt{-g_{00}g_{rr}}} \left| \frac{dg_{00}}{dr} \right|_{r=r_+} \tag{11}$$

In our case, $-g_{00}g_{rr} = 1$ and (11) leads to

$$T_H = \frac{1}{4\pi r_+} \frac{r_+^3 - l_0^3}{r_+^3 + l_0^3/2} \tag{12}$$

First, we notice that T_H vanishes at the extremal configuration, $r_+ = l_0$, which eliminates the pathological behavior of the Schwarzschild solution at the final phase of the evaporation. T_H increases with increasing radius up to a maximum value at $r_{max.} = (5 + 3\sqrt{3})^{1/3}l_0/2^{1/3}$, then approaches zero as $r_+ \to \infty$.

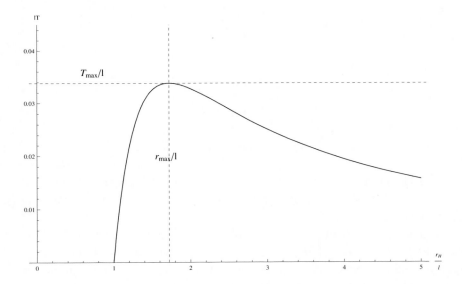

Figure 2. Plot of the Hawking temperature as a function of the horizon radius.

Another important thermodynamical quantity assigned to the BH is its entropy. After the Bekenstein/Hawking results, it is customary to identify the entropy with $1/4$ of the horizon area in Planck units. Suppose we have a Planckian BH with radius and mass given by

$$r_0 = l_P, \tag{13}$$

$$M_0 = \frac{3M_P}{4} \tag{14}$$

where, l_P and M_P are the Planck length and mass. Continuing the previous discussion, the extremal Bhs correspond to the molecular volume. In a statistical description the extremal BH should correspond to a macro-state realized by a *single* micro-state and, thus, has zero entropy.

Apart from the general assumption of the validity of the area law, one should be able to calculate it in the same way as it is calculated for a real gas, i.e., from the first law of thermodynamics. In the case of a BH, the first law is given by:

$$dM = T_H dS \tag{15}$$

From (15) one can derive that

$$dS = 4\pi \left[\frac{\partial g_{00}}{\partial M} \right]^{-1}_{r=r_+} dr_+ \tag{16}$$

For the metric (2) one finds

$$
\begin{aligned}
S \quad &= \frac{\pi}{G_N} \left(r_+^2 - l_0^2 \right) + \frac{\pi}{G_N} l_0^3 \left(\frac{1}{l_0} - \frac{1}{r_+} \right) , \\
&= \frac{A_H}{4G_N} \left(1 - \frac{V_0}{V_H} \right)
\end{aligned}
\tag{17}
$$

where,

$$A_H \equiv 4\pi r_+^2 , \tag{18}$$

$$V_H \equiv \frac{4\pi}{3} r_+^3 , \tag{19}$$

$$V_0 \equiv \frac{4\pi}{3} l_0^3 \tag{20}$$

For large BHs, far away from extremality, $V_H \gg V_0$, we recover the standard area law $S = A_H/4G_N$, but as the "quantum" regime is approached volume corrections become important and cannot be neglected.

It is crucial to remark that the integration of (16), leading to (17), is bounded from below by the radius r_0 of the extremal configuration as there are no smaller BHs.

Thus, we obtain the generalized "area law" which also gives the form of the entropy satisfying the third law. It contains further corrections induced by the presence of the minimal length. For the "bare" Schwarzschild metric there is no extremal, minimal size, configuration and the corresponding entropy is simply on fourth of the area. Assuming that this is a "universal" behavior for all BHs, leads to an inconsistency with the third law, i.e., zero-temperature extremal BHs with non-zero entropy. Thus, even in the absence of a minimal length, whenever a BH admits an extremal configuration, the correct way to calculate the entropy is by integrating the first law from the minimal radius of the extremal configuration and not from zero. The correct definition of entropy is given by the difference of the area of the non-extremal configuration and the extremal one.

2.2. Phase Transitions

In this subsection we are going to study eventual phase transitions of regular neutral BHs. We follow the analogy with finite temperature quantum field theory where different vacuum phases are studied in terms of the stationary points of effective potential. The order parameter is the vacuum expectation value of some scalar field operator expressed as a function of the temperature. Different phases correspond to different vacuum expectation values.

In our case off-shell free energy, $F^{Off.}$ plays the role of the effective potential while the order parameter is represented by the radius of the BH. Different phases correspond to different size BHs. The advantage of using the *off-shell free energy* is that T is a free parameter describing the evolution from non-equilibrium, $T \neq T_H$, to $T = T_H$ states when the BH is in equilibrium with the surrounding thermal bath.

$$F^{Off.} \equiv M - TS \tag{21}$$

We look for the extremal of $F^{Off.}$ which corresponds to equilibrium configurations.

$$F^{Off.} = \frac{1}{4G_N r_+^2} \left(2r_+^3 + l_0^3 - 4\pi r_+^4 T + 4\pi l_0^3 r_+ T \right) \ , r_+ \geq l_0 \tag{22}$$

The extrema of (22) are solutions of the condition

$$\frac{dF^{Off.}}{dr_+} = \frac{1}{2G_N r_+^3} \left(r_+^3 - l_0^3 - 4\pi r_+^4 T - 2\pi l_0^3 r_+ T \right) = 0 \tag{23}$$

Equation (23) determines the free parameter T as a function of r_+

$$T = \frac{1}{4\pi r_+} \frac{r_+^3 - l_0^3}{r_+^3 + l_0^3/2} \equiv T_H \tag{24}$$

proving the general property that the extrema of $F^{Off.}$ corresponds to BHs in thermal equilibrium with the surrounding heat bath.

If we were able to invert (24) we could find the way in which the order parameter r_+ evolves by varying T, as in the finite temperature quantum field theory. Unfortunately, the equation is fourth order and cannot be easily and transparently solved. However, we can obtain simple analytic solutions by considering the near-extremal and large radius limits for low temperature BHs.

For near extremal configurations we find

$$r_{min.} \approx l_0 \left(1 + 2\pi l_0 T \right) \tag{25}$$

while, for large BHs, away from extremality, we find

$$r_{max.} \approx \frac{1}{4\pi T} \tag{26}$$

At low temperature $r_{min.}$ and $r_{max.}$ are the local minimum and local maximum of $F^{Off.}$. Thus, near-extremal BHs are classically stable, while large BHs are unstable and decay either towards extremality or grow indefinitely without ever reaching the equilibrium.

The two extrema merge at a critical temperature $\tilde{T}$ where both (23) and

$$\frac{d^2 F^{Off.}}{dr_+^2} = \frac{1}{2G_N r_+^4}\left(3l_0^3 - 4\pi r_+^4 T + 4\pi l_0^3 r_+ T\right) \qquad (27)$$

vanish. One finds that this happens for

$$\tilde{r}_{flex.}^3 = \frac{l_0^3}{2}\left(5 + 3\sqrt{3}\right) = r_{max.}^3 \qquad (28)$$

and

$$\tilde{T} = \frac{1}{2\pi\tilde{r}_{flex.}}\frac{1}{1+\sqrt{3}} = T_H^{max.} \qquad (29)$$

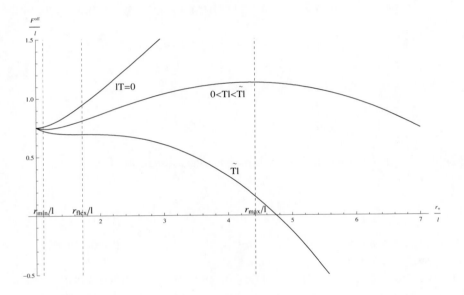

Figure 3. Plot of the off-shell free energy for different values of the temperature T.

Figure 3 summarizes the main conclusions of the previous analysis of phase transitions. At zero temperature there is a single extremal BH in equilibrium with the surrounding vacuum. As the temperature increases, even slightly, the free energy develops a local minimum and a local maximum, the first corresponds to a small, near-extremal, classically stable BH, while the second is a large classically unstable BH. In fact, the free energy is unbounded from below for large BHs which are colder than the surrounding heat bath. As a consequence they continue to grow never reaching an equilibrium configuration. This behavior follows from the "competition" between the internal energy end entropy entering $F^{Off.}$ with opposite sign. M increases linearly with r_+ while the entropy increases with r_+^2.

Thus, the negative entropy term dominate over the positive internal energy contribution beyond some critical size. This pathological behavior will be cured in the next section by introducing an Anti de Sitter background whose negative (inward) pressure will stop this unlimited expansion.

A further increase in T leads to a critical value, $\tilde{T}$, where the maximum and the minimum merge into an inflexion point. Remarkably, $\tilde{T} = T_H^{max.}$, where only one unstable BH exists.

For $T > \tilde{T}$ BHs do not exists.

The critical behavior of the system can also be inferred from the form of the heat capacity:

$$C_H \equiv \frac{\partial M}{\partial T_H} = -\frac{3\pi l_0^3}{G_N} \frac{r_+^2 \left(r_+^3 + l_0^3/2 \right)}{\left[r_+^3 - l_0^3 \left(5 + 3\sqrt{3} \right) \right] \left[r_+^3 - l_0^3 \left(5 - 3\sqrt{3} \right) \right]} \tag{30}$$

C_H diverges for $r_+ = r_{max.}$, it is positive for $l_0 \geq r_+ \geq r_{max.}$, and is negative for $r_+ > r_{max.}$. The near-extremal region has $C_H > 0$ and BHs show the normal, stable, thermodynamical behavior, while in the region $C_H < 0$ the anomalous behavior described above takes place, i.e., increasing the total mass M lowers the temperature triggering a limitless growth.

2.3. Area Quantization

The results obtained in the previous discussion indicate that there is a minimal size (extremal) BH even of Planckian dimension, as well as the corresponding minimal area. Thus, we are led to an interesting conjecture, i.e., an holographically improved "Bohr quantization" of the BH. Instead of quantizing the mass of the BH, we rather quantize its area in terms of the minimal area of the extremal configuration

$$A_H = nA_0 = 4\pi n\, l_0^2\,, \qquad n = 1\,,2\,,3\,,\ldots \tag{31}$$

It follows from (31) that the radius of the horizon increases according with

$$r_H = \sqrt{n}\, l_0 \tag{32}$$

By inserting (32) into (41) we obtain the quantized mass spectrum as :

$$M_n = \frac{n^{3/2} + 1/2}{2G_N n} l_0 = \frac{2}{3} M_0 \frac{n^{3/2} + 1/2}{n} \tag{33}$$

For large n. highly excited BH states have mass given by

$$M_n \approx \frac{2}{3} M_0\, n^{1/2} \tag{34}$$

and the difference between successive mass levels vanishes as $n^{-1/2}$. This is the region where the thermal picture for the Hawking radiation makes sense since the mass levels become practically continuous.

On the other hand, in the truly quantum regime transitions occur discontinuously through emission of single quanta $\hbar\omega$ given by the mass difference between nearby levels:

$$\Delta M_n = \frac{2}{3}M_0 \left[(n+1)^{1/2} - n^{1/2} \right] \equiv \hbar\omega_n \tag{35}$$

In this picture, the final stage of BH decay resembles more the discontinuous spectra of the atomic transitions, than a thermal radiation from an hot body.

3.   AdS Black Hole and Criticality

The unboundedness from below of the free energy, we found in the previous section, is specific to the asymptotically flat boundary conditions satisfied by the the metric (2). To cure the BH instability towards a limitless growth one introduces a negative cosmological constant in the Einstein equations and solve them with the energy-momentum tensor (10).

From a physical point of view, a negative cosmological constant represents a positive (inward pushing) vacuum pressure

$$p \equiv -\frac{\Lambda}{8\pi G_N} = \frac{3}{8\pi G_N a^2} \tag{36}$$

making an unbounded inflation energetically disfavored.

A further motivation for studying AdS BHs is that in higher dimensions they have a pivotal role in the implementation of the AdS_5/CFT duality [26, 27, 28]. This kind of duality offers a powerful tool to tackle non-perturbative features of a variety of physical systems ranging from the quark-gluon plasma [29] to fluids [30] and super-conductors [31]. The strong-coupling regime of a conformal field theory living on the flat boundary of AdS_5 is mapped by duality into the weak-coupling quantum string theory (quantum gravity) in the $AdS_5 \times S_5$ bulk. This amazing spin-off of string theory connects $4D$ physics in flat space-time to quantum gravity in AdS_5 and provides a beautiful realization of the Holographic Principle [12, 13].

Sticking to our toy-model, we find the line element

$$ds^2 = -\left(1 - 2G_N\frac{M(r)}{r} + \frac{r^2}{a^2}\right)dt^2 + \left(1 - 2G_N\frac{M(r)}{r} + \frac{r^2}{a^2}\right)^{-1}dr^2 + r^2 d\Omega^2 \tag{37}$$

where $\Lambda \equiv -3/a^2$ and

$$M(r) \equiv M \frac{r_+^3}{r_+^3 + l_0^3\left(1 + 3l_0^2/a^2\right)/2} \tag{38}$$

We have introduced a new free parameter in the model, i.e., the vacuum pressure, which will play, together with the temperature, an important role in determining the phases of the system.

The two length scale l_0 and a rule the short and large distance behavior of the metric, respectively. The short distance form of the metric is again of the type

$$ds^2 = -\left(1 - \frac{\Lambda}{3}r^2\right)dt^2 + \left(1 - \frac{\Lambda}{3}r^2\right)^{-1}dr^2 + r^2 d\Omega^2 \tag{39}$$

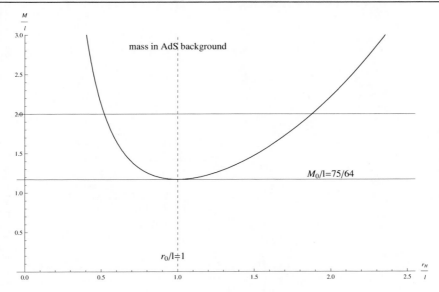

Figure 4. Plot of the function in (41).

where

$$\frac{\Lambda}{3} = \frac{2G_N M}{l_0^3 \left(1 + 3l_0^2/a^2\right)/2} - \frac{1}{a^2} \tag{40}$$

As the three parameters M, l_0, a are free, Λ can be positive, negative or even zero. In any case the metric is singularity free being either deSitter, Anti deSitter, or Minkowski.

The existence of horizons can be seen plotting the BH mass given by

$$M = \frac{r_+^3 + l_0^3 \left(1 + 3l_0^2/a^2\right)/2}{2G_N r_+^2} \left(1 + \frac{r_+^2}{a^2}\right) \tag{41}$$

as a function of r_+. The plot is given in figure (4)

$$\frac{\partial M}{\partial r_+} = \frac{1}{2G_N r_+^3} \left[r_+^3 \left(1 + 3r_+^2/a^2\right) - l_0^3 \left(1 + 3l_0^2/a^2\right)\right] \tag{42}$$

The temperature is given as

$$T_H = \frac{1}{4\pi r_+} \frac{r_+^3 \left(1 + 3r_+^2/a^2\right) - l_0^3 \left(1 + 3l_0^2/a^2\right)}{r_+^3 + l_0^3 \left(1 + 3l_0^2/a^2\right)/2} \tag{43}$$

The entropy turns out to be

$$\begin{aligned}
S &= \frac{\pi}{G_N} \left(r_+^2 - l_0^2\right) + \frac{\pi}{G_N} l_0^3 \left(1 + \frac{3l_0^2}{a^2}\right) \left(\frac{1}{l_0} - \frac{1}{r_+}\right), \\
&= \frac{A_H}{4G_N} \left(1 - \frac{V_0}{V_H}\right) + \frac{3\pi}{G_N} \frac{l_0^4}{a^2} \left(1 - \frac{l_0}{r_+}\right) \tag{44}
\end{aligned}$$

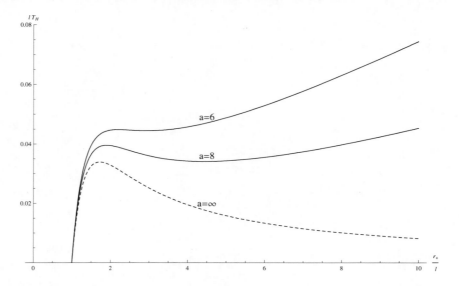

Figure 5. Plot of the Hawking temperature for different values of the vacuum pressure. The inflexion point marks the transition between low/high pressure regimes.

$$
\begin{aligned}
F^{Off.} &= \frac{1}{4G_N r_+^2} \left[2r_+^3 + l_0^3 \left(1 + 3l_0^2/a^2 \right) \right] \left(1 + \frac{r_+^2}{a^2} \right) \\
&\quad - \frac{\pi T}{G_N} \left[r_+^2 - l_0^2 + l_0^3 \left(1 + \frac{3l_0^2}{a^2} \right) \left(\frac{1}{l_0} - \frac{1}{r_+} \right) \right]
\end{aligned}
\tag{45}
$$

Let us note that (45) for large r_+ can be approximated with

$$
F^{Off.} \approx \frac{r_+^3}{8G_N a^2} - \frac{\pi T}{G_N} r_+^2
\tag{46}
$$

Equation (46) shows how large radius configurations are energetically disfavored as they imply a net increase of the free energy. The negative increase from the entropy term is no more able to compensate for positive increase of internal energy.

$$
\begin{aligned}
\frac{dF^{Off.}}{dr_+} &= \frac{1}{2G_N r_+^3} \left[r_+^3 + 3r_+^5/a^2 - l_0^3 \left(1 + 3l_0^2/a^2 \right) \right. \\
&\quad \left. - 4\pi r_+ T \left(r_+^3 + l_0^3 \left(1 + 3l_0^2/a^2 \right) /2 \right) \right]
\end{aligned}
\tag{47}
$$

As previously discussed, $\frac{dF^{Off.}}{dr_+} = 0 \Rightarrow T = T_H$.

3.1. "Low" Vacuum Pressure Phases

The extrema of free energy indicate existence of both *multiple* and *single* regular BHs for different values of the temperature. The alternation of single/multiple states is the signature

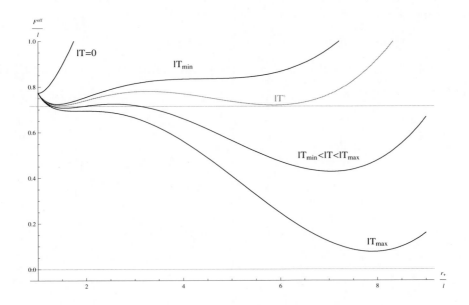

Figure 6. Plot of the off-shell free energy for different values of the temperature T in the low-pressure regime showing the existence of different phases. The critical curve, for $T = T^*$ is shown in magenta.

of a first order phase transition, as in finite temperature quantum field theory, to which we refer.

It turns out that single/multiple BH transitions occur at the inflection points of free energy (extremal points of T_H). Thus, the following scenario is in place in the low-pressure regime $a \geq a_c$:

1. $T = 0$. BH is in the *frozen single state*. The only ground state is the extremal configuration with $r_+ = r_- = l_0$.

2. $0 \leq T \leq T_{min}$. BHs are in the *cold single* state of radius $l_0 < r_+ < r_{min}$. This is due to the effect of the minimal length l_0.

3. At $T = T_{min}$ an inflexion point appears in F^{off} at $r_+ = r_{min}$.

4. $T_{min} < T < T^*$. New local minimum develops and the system splits into two co-existing states. The small near-extremal BH is energetically favored.

5. $T = T^*$ the two minima become degenerate and the system is in a *mixed state*. Both BHs have the same free energy.

6. $T^* < T < T_{max}$ large BHs become stable, while near-extremal BHs are only locally stable.

7. $T = T_{max}$ The near-extremal minimum merges with the local maximum. There is a new transition from multiple to a single BH state.

8. $T > T_{max}$ there is *high temperature, single, stable* BH.

The above scenario describes *first order* phase transitions from single to multiple BHs at $T = T_{min}$ and $T = T_{max}$.

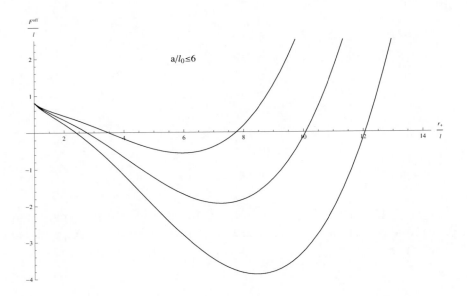

Figure 7. Plot of the off-shell free energy for different values of the temperature T in the high-pressure regime, $a/l_0 \leq 6$.

3.2. "High" Vacuum Pressure Phases

One can see that the first order phase transitions take place in the low vacuum pressure regime, only. In fact, the two parameters of the theory have "opposite" effects i.e., l_0 dominates short-range distance behavior and lowers T_{max}, while a dominates long-range region of r_+ and thus raises T_{min}.

It is reasonable to expect that, at the certain point, these two opposing effects will meet creating an *inflexion* point of the temperature. The confirmation of our conjecture is shown in Figure 5.

In terms of the free energy the same effect can be seen in the Figure 7, where a single minimum exists beyond the inflexion point $a = 2.88\, l_0$. Varying T only lowers the *position* of the *single* minimum.

A complex phase structure is a general feature of several types of BH where some characteristic length scale is present in the metric [32, 33, 34, 35].

4. Gaussian Regularization

In the first part of this chapter we introduced an "ad hoc" method of eliminating curvature singularities using ideas usually adopted in quantum field theory, i. e. introducing a suitable short-distance cut-off. However, there is another approach in QFT achieving the same goal but having a profound physical significance. For example, UV infinities in Feynman diagrams (beyond the tree-level) can be eliminated by replacing the bare (euclidean) propagator with an exponentially damped one [36, 37, 38, 39]

$$\frac{1}{k^2 + m^2} \longrightarrow \frac{e^{-k^2/2\Lambda}}{k^2 + m^2} \tag{48}$$

The meaning of the above substitution is to replace a divergent two-point Green function (in coordinate space) with a regular one solving the inhomogeneous equation

$$\left(\partial^2 + m^2 \right) G_\Lambda \left(x - y \right) = \frac{1}{(2\pi\Lambda)^2} \exp \left(-\frac{(x-y)^2}{4\Lambda} \right) \tag{49}$$

Equation (49) shows that physical particles with propagator (48) are not matter "points", but are smeared Gaussian energy distributions. In quantum mechanics Gaussian wave packets represents minimal uncertainty states, i.e., the closest one can get to a classical particle.

The approach of substituting point-like particles with Gaussian matter distributions has been carried out in a number of papers in order to describe quantum mechanics and in QFT in *coordinate* non-commutative space(time), characterized by

$$[\, x^\mu, x^\nu \,] = i\theta^{\mu\nu} \tag{50}$$

where l_0 can be related to Lorentz invariant quantity

$$l_0^2 \propto \sqrt{\theta^{\mu\nu} \theta_{\mu\nu}} \tag{51}$$

It is already widely accepted that space-time at short distances is no more modeled by a smooth manifold but something completely different. Our ignorance about the space-time Planckian phase leaves room for different hypothesis, e.g., string, loop, fractal, non-commutative, foamy phases, etc., all sharing the existence of a characteristic length scale. The introduction of l_0 as the minimal width of a Gaussian distribution is motivated by non-commutativity of coordinates (50), much like the non-commutativity of phase space coordinates in QM is characterized by $\hbar$.

By accepting this idea, one wonders how to implement it in the case of gravity. At first glance, one could think of modifying the very definition of the metric tensor to incorporate l_0 in the space-time fabric, e.g., replacing the ordinary product of functions by the star-product. This approach, apart heavily complicating Einstein equations, has the basic flaw that any perturbative expansion in theta, truncated at a finite order, leads to the loss of non-locality of the original theory. The resulting solutions contain all the pathologies of the commutative theory (curvature singularities) in spite of having introduced l_0 from the very beginning.

Alternatively, we argued that instead of changing the space-time geometry the effects of l_0 can be implemented through the matter source. The line of reasoning is the following.

Metric field is a geometrical structure defined over an underlying manifold. Curvature measures the strength of the metric field, i.e., is the response to the presence of a mass-energy distribution. On the other hand, energy-momentum density determines space-time curvature. Thus, we conclude that in General Relativity the effects of l_0 can be taken into account by keeping the standard form of the Einstein tensor in the l.h.s. of the field equations and introducing a modified energy-momentum tensor as a source in the r.h.s.

Thus, we choose the mass density of a static, spherically symmetric, smeared, particle-like gravitational source as [25]

$$\rho(r) \equiv M\sigma(r) = \left(\frac{3}{l_0}\right)^3 \frac{M}{(4\pi)^{3/2}} \exp\left(-\frac{9r^2}{4l_0^2}\right) \tag{52}$$

By solving Einstein equations with (52) as a matter source, we find the line element [5]

$$ds^2 = -\left(1 - \frac{2MG_N}{r}\frac{\gamma(3/2;9r^2/4l_0^2)}{\Gamma(3/2)}\right)dt^2$$
$$+ \left(1 - \frac{2MG_N}{r}\frac{\gamma(3/2;9r^2/4l_0^2)}{\Gamma(3/2)}\right)^{-1} dr^2 + r^2 d\Omega^2 \tag{53}$$

where,

$$\gamma(3/2;x) \equiv \int_0^x du\, u^{1/2}e^{-u} \tag{54}$$

Strictly speaking, the density (52) is non-vanishing everywhere, even if it quickly drops below any measurable value at few orders of l_0. However, this may rise the question if a BH can be formed by such a smeared distribution. In order to answer this question we evoke the *hoop conjecture* [40] and adapt it to the present situation [6]. It means that we define a *mean radius* of the mass distribution as

$$<r> \equiv 4\pi \int_0^\infty dr r^2 \sigma(r) r = \frac{4}{3\sqrt{\pi}} l_0 \tag{55}$$

the hoop conjecture assumes that whenever, for a given total mass M,

$$<r> \le r_H(M) \tag{56}$$

where, r_H is the radius of the eventual Killing horizon determined from (53), the metric (53) will describe a BH.

The analysis of the function

$$M = \frac{r_H}{2G_N}\frac{\Gamma(3/2)}{\gamma(3/2;9r_H^2/4l_0^2)} \tag{57}$$

shows (see Figure) that it admits an inner, r_-, Cauchy and an outer, $r_+ (\ge r_-)$ Killing horizon, which merge into a single degenerate horizon, $r_\pm \to r_0$, in the extremal case. The radius of the extremal BH is again $r_0 = l_0$, as in the toy-model case, while the mass is

$$M_0 = \frac{l_0}{2G_N}\frac{\Gamma(3/2)}{\gamma(3/2;9/4)} \tag{58}$$

---

[5]The numerical coefficients have been numerically determined to have $r_0 = l_0$.
[6]A quantum formulation of the hoop conjecture has been recently proposed in [41].

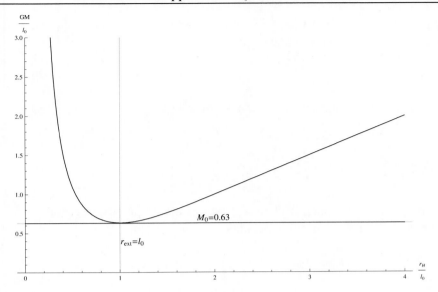

Figure 8. Plot of the mass M as a function of the radius r_H of the horizon.

Thus, we find

$$< r >< r_0 \leq r_+ \tag{59}$$

which show that even in the extremal case the mean radius of the mass distribution is smaller that the radius of the horizon. Enough mass is confined within the horizon in order to sustain the existence of the BH.

Furthermore, the metric (53) exhibits the short-distance behavior of the deSitter form with no singularity at the origin. This can be inferred from the behavior of the incomplete gamma function $\gamma(3/2; x)$ for small argument

$$\gamma(3/2; x^2) \approx x^3 , \qquad x \longrightarrow 0 \tag{60}$$

4.1. "Bohr Quantization"

A closer look at equation (52) suggests an intriguing analogy with the probability density of the the ground-state wave function of an isotropic, 3D, harmonic oscillator

$$\sigma(r) \longleftrightarrow |\psi_{000}(r)|^2 \tag{61}$$

where,

$$\psi_{000}(r) \propto e^{-mr^2\omega/2} \tag{62}$$

is the ground state wave function. In order to identify m and ω with the corresponding quantities in (52), we notice that

$$m\omega = \frac{9}{8l_0^2} \tag{63}$$

and the mass of the extremal BH represents the minimum energy of the equivalent harmonic oscillator, i.e., M_0 is the zero-point energy

$$\frac{3}{2}\omega = M_0 \tag{64}$$

By solving the two equations (63), (64) we find

$$\omega = \frac{2}{3}M_0 \, , \tag{65}$$

$$m = \frac{27}{8}\frac{1}{l_0^2 M_0} \tag{66}$$

The non-extremal BH quantized configurations are assumed to be, the $l = 0$ excited states of the corresponding harmonic oscillator:

$$M_n = M_0 \left(1 + \frac{2}{3}n \right) \, , \quad n = 0\,,2\,,4\,,\ldots \tag{67}$$

Due to the spherical symmetry only even oscillator states are allowed. Thus, in this new formulation of quantum BHs, the extremal configuration is pure *collapsed zero-point energy*, and the excited states are non extremal BHs with discrete masses given by (67).

The analogy with the harmonic oscillator [42] has to be reconciled with the requirement that even excited BH states keep the simplest geometric structure consisting of either a single extremal configuration or a non-extremal BH having one internal Cauchy horizon and one external Killing horizon only. To achieve this, instead of using the complete excited harmonic oscillator wave function, we propose to keep only the highest power of the Laguerre polynomials in the energy density[7]

$$\rho_n\left(r \right) \equiv M_n \sigma_n(r) = \frac{M_n}{\Gamma(n + 3/2)} \frac{3^{2n+3} r^{2n}}{2^{2n+4} \pi l_0^{2n+3}} e^{-9r^2/4l_0^2} \tag{68}$$

Therefore, the effective geometry describing "quantized" BHs is still described by the equation (53) with the exception that the continuous parameter M is replaced by its discrete version given by (67)

$$ds_n^2 = -\left(1 - \frac{2M_n G_N}{r} \frac{\gamma(n + 3/2\,;9r^2/4l_0^2)}{\Gamma(n + 3/2)} \right) dt^2$$
$$+ \left(1 - \frac{2M_n G_N}{r} \frac{\gamma(n + 3/2\,;9r^2/4l_0^2)}{\Gamma(n + 3/2)} \right)^{-1} dr^2 + r^2 d\Omega^2 \tag{69}$$

For each n the existence of the horizons is given by

$$M_n\left(r_H \right) = \frac{r_H}{2G_N} \frac{\Gamma(n + 3/2)}{\gamma(n + 3/2\,;9r_H^2/4l_0^2)} \, , \tag{70}$$

$$M_n = M_0 \left(1 + \frac{2}{3}n \right) \tag{71}$$

---

[7]A Maxwell-type energy disitribution like (1) has been recently used to model the final stage of the gravitational collapse of a "thick shell" of matter [43]. Here we shall use the same type of distribution in a different way.

However, BH being described as a quantum system one has to verify the average radius of the mass distribution is inside the corresponding horizon radius. This is known as the quantum "hoop conjecture".

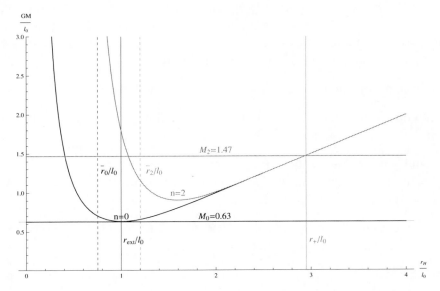

Figure 9. Plot of the ground state $n = 0$ (black) and the first excited state $n = 2$ (red). Horizontal lines correspond to the quantized masses M_0, M_2. Solid vertical lines are the Killing horizons. Dashed vertical lines represents $< r >_n$ of the mass distribution for $n = 0 , 2$. They show as the hoop conjecture is satisfied.

$$< r >_n \equiv 4\pi \int_0^\infty dr r^2 \sigma_n(r) r \qquad (72)$$

$$< r >_n = \frac{2l_0}{3} \frac{\Gamma(n+2)}{\Gamma(n+3/2)} \qquad (73)$$

The Figure 9 below summarizes the main characteristics of the quantized BHs described above. The difference between the classical BH given in Figure 1. While in Figure 1 horizons are obtained making an arbitrary cut parallel to the r_H-axis, since M is a continuous parameter, in the quantized case we have distinct graphs for any value of n and for each curve a *single* horizontal line $M = M_n$. Only for $n = 0$ there is a an extremal BH, while for $n \geq 2$ we have non-degenerate BHs corresponding to excited states. For any value of n the hoop conjecture, $< r > < r_+$, is satisfied.

5. Conclusion and Discussion

In this chapter we have described a generalization of the standard Schwarzschild geometry which takes into account the presence of a "minimal" length l_0 which should be present in a quantum, to be, formulation of gravity. It is widely believe, from different points of view, that such a parameter should be necessarily incorporated in a physically meaningful formulation of quantized gravity. In the first part, we have restricted ourself to simple, toy-model, of regular BH in order to display novel features of such a theory in a relatively transparent way. It has been claimed [44] that the way in which l_0 is introduced is not essential and the same features are common to different models. In fact, we showed in the second part that a more complicated and realistic model shares basic features with the simpler toy-model. The effects of l_0, in both models, are:

- to replace the curvature singularity in $r = 0$ by a regular deSitter core;

- to introduce a lower limit to the BH mass in the form of an extremal configuration, even in the absence of charge and angular momentum;

- to identify the radius of the extremal configuration with l_0, in agreement with the UV self-complete quantum gravity hypothesis, where sub-Planckian distances are screened by (extremal) BH formation;

- to provide a consistent final state for BH decay through Hawking radiation in the form of zero temperature extremal BH remnant;

- to remove unphysical negative heat capacity during the final stage of BH evaporation;

- to introduce corrections to the area law which is strictly valid for point-like matter sources only.

From the technical point of view, l_0 was introduced first in the source term in the Einstein equations through the properly chosen smeared matter distribution. In this picture l_0 measures the de-localization, of the otherwise point-like source, induced by quantum gravitational fluctuations of the underlying space-time manifold. The important advantage of this approach is that one can obtain *exact* solutions of the Einstein equations. Alternative approaches, e.g., based on star-product, cannot achieve the same goal since one is forced to perform truncated perturbative expansion in l_0 suffering from the same pathologies l_0 is expected to have cured.

The use of a Gaussian energy distribution suggests an intriguing analogy with the ground state of the quantum harmonic oscillator. This has led us to envisage a possible Bohr-like quantization scheme of our classical regular solution. This has been described in the last part of this chapter, where the following quantum picture emerges:

- the ground state is an extremal BH of size l_0, with mass M_0, which is the analogue of the harmonic oscillator zero-point energy.

- Excited states are non-extremal BHs with mass $M_n = M_0(1 + 2n/3)$.

- The semi-classical Hawking picture of thermally radiating BHs remains valid for large n, while it becomes modified for small n. In the truly quantum regime the continuous thermal spectrum turns into a discontinuous spectrum corresponding to the transitions between low lying mass levels.

- Is it self-consistent to interpret the above excited states as BHs?

  Our answer is yes, because they satisfy the quantum version of the "hoop-conjecture", i.e. the mean radius of the mass distribution is always smaller that the corresponding radius of the horizon.

In view of the quantum picture described above, one can envisage a quantum BH of mass M_n as a "bound-state" of $n = 2, 4, 6, \ldots$ quanta of energy $\hbar\omega = 2M_0c^2/3$. The ground-state, or "*zero-point*" BH is given by the extremal configuration with $n = 0$ and $M = M_0$.

In the last part of this chapter, we were interested in the quantum aspects of regular BHs and have not described the thermodynamical features of the metric (53), which however can be found in [25].

6. Appendix: Regular Coulomb Potential

In Section (2) we regularized the Newtonian potential through the substitution (1). As the Coulomb potential "suffers" from the same "illness" in $r = 0$, one is tempted to regularize it in the same way., i.e. we propose the following substitution

$$V_C(r) \longrightarrow V_{C\,reg.}(r) = -\frac{e}{4\pi\varepsilon_0}\frac{r^2}{r^3 + l_0^3/2} \tag{74}$$

The limiting behavior of $V_{C\,reg.}$ is:

$$V_{C\,reg.}(r) \longrightarrow V_C(r), \qquad r \to \infty, \tag{75}$$

$$V_{C\,reg.}(r) \longrightarrow -\frac{e}{2\pi\varepsilon_0}\frac{r^2}{l_0^3}, \qquad r \to 0 \tag{76}$$

In particular, at short distance the attractive ordinary Coulomb potential turns into a parabolic barrier surrounding the origin. Thus, only positive energy, unbound charges can reach the origin.

$$\frac{dV_{C\,reg.}}{dr} = 0 \longrightarrow r_{min.} = l_0, \quad V_C(r_{min.}) = -\frac{e}{6\pi\varepsilon_0 l_0} \tag{77}$$

In the presence of a minimal length, the attractive Coulomb potential develops a minimum at $r = r_{min.}$ and a central hard core in an analogous manner as the Newtonian potential in the gravitational case.

A more physically motivated regularization starts from replacing a point-like charge density with a smeared Gaussian like distribution given by

$$\rho(r) = \frac{e}{(4\pi l_0^2)^{3/2}} \exp\left(-\frac{r^2}{4l_0^2}\right) \tag{78}$$

Solving the Poisson equation one finds

$$V_{C\,reg.} = \frac{e}{r}\frac{\gamma(1/2\,;\,r^2/4\theta)}{\Gamma(1/2)} \tag{79}$$

and the corresponding electric field, which is the analogue of the gravitational curvature, is regular in $r = 0$

$$E_{C\,reg.} = \frac{e}{r^2} \frac{\gamma(3/2\,;\,r^2/4\theta)}{\Gamma(3/2)} \tag{80}$$

This form of the electric field has been used as source in the Einstein equations to obtain the charged extension [45, 46] of the BH we discussed in Section (4).

References

[1] K. Kiefer, *"Quantum Gravity"*, OUP Oxford; (2012)

[2] A. Hagar, "Discrete or Continuous?: The Quest for Fundamental Length in Modern Physics" Cambridge University Press (2014)

[3] M. Fontanini, E. Spallucci and T. Padmanabhan, *Phys. Lett. B* 633, 627 (2006)

[4] A. Aurilia and E. Spallucci, *Adv. High Energy Phys.* 2013, 531696 (2013)

[5] A. Smailagic and E. Spallucci, *Phys. Lett. B* 688, 82 (2010)

[6] P. Nicolini, *Int. J. Mod. Phys. A* 24, 1229 (2009)

[7] S. W. Hawking, *Commun. Math. Phys.* 43, 199 (1975)

[8] N. D. Birrell, P. C. W. Davies, *"Quantum Fields in Curved Space"* Cambridge University Press; Reprint edition (1984)

[9] S. A. Fulling, *"Aspects of Quantum Field Theory in Curved Spacetime"* Cambridge University Press (1989)

[10] L. Parker and D. Toms, *"Quantum Field Theory in Curved Spacetime: Quantized Fields and Gravity"* Cambridge University Press (2009)

[11] S. Hollands and R. M. Wald, *"Quantum fields in curved spacetime,"* arXiv:1401.2026 [gr-qc].

[12] L. Susskind, *J. Math. Phys.* 36, 6377 (1995)

[13] L. Susskind and E. Witten, *"The Holographic bound in anti-de Sitter space,"* arXiv:hep-th/9805114.

[14] F. Nasseri, *Gen. Rel. Grav.* 37, 2223 (2005)

[15] F. Nasseri, *Int. J. Mod. Phys. D* 15, 1113 (2006)

[16] A. Bonanno and M. Reuter, *Phys. Rev. D* 62, 043008 (2000)

[17] S. A. Hayward, *Phys. Rev. Lett.* 96, 031103 (2006)

[18] E. Spallucci and A. Smailagic, *Phys. Lett. B* 709, 266 (2012)

[19] J. Mureika, P. Nicolini and E. Spallucci, *Phys. Rev. D* 85, 106007 (2012)

[20] P. Nicolini, J. Mureika, E. Spallucci, E. Winstanley and M. Bleicher, *"Production and evaporation of Planck scale black holes at the LHC,"* arXiv:1302.2640 [hep-th].

[21] E. Spallucci and S. Ansoldi, *Phys. Lett. B* 701, 471 (2011)

[22] G. Dvali and C. Gomez, *"Self-Completeness of Einstein Gravity,"* arXiv:1005.3497 [hep-th].

[23] G. Dvali, G. F. Giudice, C. Gomez and A. Kehagias, *JHEP* 1108, 108 (2011)

[24] P. Nicolini and E. Spallucci, *Adv. High Energy Phys.* 2014, 805684 (2014)

[25] P. Nicolini, A. Smailagic and E. Spallucci, *Phys. Lett. B* 632, 547 (2006)

[26] J. M. Maldacena, *Adv. Theor. Math. Phys.* 2, 231 (1998) [*Int. J. Theor. Phys.* 38, 1113 (1999)]

[27] E. Witten, *Adv. Theor. Math. Phys.* 2, 505 (1998)

[28] E. Witten, *Adv. Theor. Math. Phys.* 2, 253 (1998)

[29] R. C. Myers, S. E. Vazquez, *Class. Quant. Grav.* 25, 114008 (2008).

[30] N. Ambrosetti, J. Charbonneau and S. Weinfurtner, *"The Fluid/gravity correspondence*: Lectures notes from the 2008 Summer School on Particles, Fields, and Strings,"* arXiv:0810.2631 [gr-qc].

[31] S. A. Hartnoll, *Class. Quant. Grav.* 26, 224002 (2009)

[32] D. Kubiznak and R. B. Mann, *JHEP* 1207, 033 (2012)

[33] A. Smailagic and E. Spallucci, *Int. J. Mod. Phys. D* 22, 1350010 (2013)

[34] E. Spallucci and A. Smailagic, *Phys. Lett. B* 723, 436 (2013)

[35] E. Spallucci and A. Smailagic, *J. Grav.* 2013, 525696 (2013)

[36] A. Smailagic and E. Spallucci, *J. Phys. A* 36, L467 (2003)

[37] A. Smailagic and E. Spallucci, *J. Phys. A* 36, L517 (2003)

[38] A. Smailagic and E. Spallucci, *J. Phys. A* 37, 1 (2004) [*Erratum-ibid. A* 37, 7169 (2004)]

[39] E. Spallucci, A. Smailagic and P. Nicolini, *Phys. Rev. D* 73, 084004 (2006)

[40] K. S. Thorne, *Nonspherical gravitational collapse, a short review*, in *J R Klauder, Magic Without Magic*, Freeman, San Francisco 1972, 231-258.

[41] R. Casadio, O. Micu and F. Scardigli, *Phys. Lett. B* 732, 105 (2014)

[42] R. Casadio and A. Orlandi, *JHEP* 1308, 025 (2013)

[43] P. Nicolini, A. Orlandi and E. Spallucci, *Adv. High Energy Phys.* 2013, 812084 (2013)

[44] T. G. Rizzo, *JHEP* 0609, 021 (2006)

[45] S. Ansoldi, P. Nicolini, A. Smailagic and E. Spallucci, *Phys. Lett. B* 645, 261 (2007)

[46] E. Spallucci, A. Smailagic and P. Nicolini, *Phys. Lett. B* 670, 449 (2009)

In: Advances in Black Holes Research
Editor: Abraham Barton

ISBN: 978-1-63463-168-6
© 2015 Nova Science Publishers, Inc.

Chapter 2

PHILOSOPHICAL ISSUES OF BLACK HOLES

Gustavo E. Romero[*]
Instituto Argentino de Radioastronomia (IAR),
Casilla de Correos, Provincia de Buenos Aires, Argentina

Abstract

Black holes are extremely relativistic objects. Physical processes around them occur in a regime where the gravitational field is extremely intense. Under such conditions, our representations of space, time, gravity, and thermodynamics are pushed to their limits. In such a situation philosophical issues naturally arise. In this chapter I review some philosophical questions related to black holes. In particular, the relevance of black holes for the metaphysical dispute between presentists and eternalists, the origin of the second law of thermodynamics and its relation to black holes, the problem of information, black holes and hypercomputing, the nature of determinisim, and the breakdown of predictability in black hole space-times. I maintain that black hole physics can be used to illuminate some important problems in the border between science and philosophy, either epistemology and ontology.

PACS 04.70.Bw, 97.60.Lf, 98.80.-k, 01.70.+w

Keywords: Black holes, cosmology, philosophy of science

1. The Philosophical Importance of Black Holes

Black holes are the most extreme objects known in the universe. Our representations of physical laws reach their limits in them. The strange phenomena that occur around black holes put to the test our basic conceptions of space, time, determinism, irreversibility, information, and causality. It is then not surprising that the investigation of black holes has philosophical impact in areas as diverse as ontology, epistemology, and theory construction. In black holes, in a very definite sense, we can say that philosophy meets experiment. But, alas, philosophers have almost paid no attention to the problems raised by the existence of black holes in the real world (for a notable and solitary exception see Weingard 1979; a

---

[*]E-mail address: romero@iar-conicet.gov.ar

recent discussion of some ontological implications of black holes can be found in Romero & Pérez 2014).

The purpose of this chapter is to palliate this omission and to provide a survey of some important philosophical issues related to black holes. I do not purport to deliver an exhaustive study; such a task would demand a whole book devoted to the topic. Rather, I would like to set path for future research, calling the attention to some specific problems.

In the next section I introduce the concept of a black hole. I do this from a space-time point of view, without connection to Newtonian analogies. Black holes are not black stars; they are fully relativistic objects and can be understood only from a relativistic perspective. Hence, I start saying a few things about space-time and relativity.

In the remaining sections of the chapter I present and discuss several philosophical issues raised by the existence and properties of black holes. In particular, I discuss what happens with determinism and predictability in black holes space-times, the implications of the existence of black holes for ontological views of time and the nature of reality, the role of black holes in the irreversibility we observe in the universe, issues related to information and whether it can be destroyed in black holes, the apparent breakdown of causality inside black holes, and, finally, the role played, if any, by black holes in the future of the universe.

2. What Is a Black Hole?

A black hole is a region of space-time, so I start introducing the concept of space-time (Minkowski 1908).

Definition. *Space-time is the emergent of the ontological composition of all events .*

Events can be considered as primitives or can be derived from things as changes in their properties if things are taken as ontologically prior. Both representations are equivalent since things can be construed as bundles of events (Romero 2013b). Since composition is not a formal operation but an ontological one [1], space-time is neither a concept nor an abstraction, but an emergent entity. As any entity, space-time can be represented by a concept. The usual representation of space-time is given by a 4-dimensional real manifold E equipped with a metric field g_{ab}:

$$\text{ST} \,\hat{=}\, \langle E, g_{ab} \rangle \,.$$

It is important to stress that space-time *is not* a manifold (i.e. a mathematical construct) but the "totality" of events. A specific model of space-time requires the specification of the source of the metric field. This is done through another field, called the "energy-momentum" tensor field T_{ab}. Hence, a model of space-time is:

$$M_{\text{ST}} = \langle E, g_{ab}, T_{ab} \rangle \,.$$

---

[1]For instance, a human body is composed of cells, but is not just a mere collection of cells since it has emergent properties and specific functions far more complex than those of the individual components.

The relation between these two tensor fields is given by field equations, which represent a basic physical law. The metric field specifies the geometry of space-time. The energy-momentum field represents the potential of change (i.e., of event generation) in space-time. All this can be cast into in the following axioms (Romero 2014b) [2].

P1 − Syntactic. The set E is a C^∞ differentiable, 4-dimensional, real pseudo-Riemannian manifold.

P2 − Syntactic. The metric structure of E is given by a tensor field of rank 2, g_{ab}, in such a way that the differential distance ds between two events is:

$$ds^2 = g_{ab}dx^a dx^b.$$

P3 − Syntactic. The tangent space of E at any point is Minkowskian, i.e., its metric is given by a symmetric tensor η_{ab} of rank 2 and trace -2.

P4 − Syntactic. The metric of E is determined by a rank 2 tensor field T_{ab} through the following field equations:

$$G_{ab} - g_{ab}\Lambda = \kappa T_{ab}, \tag{1}$$

where G_{ab} is a second rank tensor whose components are functions of the second derivatives of the metric. Both Λ and κ are constants.

P5 − Semantic. The elements of E represent physical events.

P6 − Semantic. Space-time is represented by an ordered pair $\langle E,\ g_{ab}\rangle$:

$$\mathrm{ST} \hat{=} \langle E,\ g_{ab}\rangle .$$

P7 − Semantic. There is a non-geometrical field represented by a 2-rank tensor field T_{ab} on the manifold E.

P8 − Semantic. A specific model of space-time is given by:

$$M_{\mathrm{ST}} = \langle E, g_{ab}, T_{ab}\rangle .$$

So far no mention has been made of the gravitational field. The sketched theory is purely ontological, and hence, cannot be yet identified with General Relativity. To formulate the field equations we introduce the Einstein tensor:

$$G_{ab} \equiv R_{ab} - \frac{1}{2}Rg_{ab}, \tag{2}$$

---

[2]I distinguish purely syntactic from semantic axioms. The former establish relations between symbols and formal concepts. The latter, relations between concepts and elements of the reality.

where R_{ab} is the Ricci tensor formed from second derivatives of the metric and $R \equiv g^{ab}R_{ab}$ is the Ricci scalar. The geodesic equations for a test particle free in the gravitational field are:

$$\frac{d^2x^a}{d\lambda^2} + \Gamma^a_{bc}\frac{dx^b}{d\lambda}\frac{dx^c}{d\lambda},$$

(3)

with λ an affine parameter and Γ^a_{bc} the affine connection, given by:

$$\Gamma^a_{bc} = \frac{1}{2}g^{ad}(\partial_b g_{cd} + \partial_c g_{bd} - \partial_d g_{bc}).$$

(4)

The affine connection is not a tensor, but can be used to build a tensor that is directly associated with the curvature of space-time: the Riemann tensor. The form of the Riemann tensor for an affine-connected manifold can be obtained through a coordinate transformation $x^a \to \bar{x}^a$ that makes the affine connection to vanish everywhere, i.e.

$$\bar{\Gamma}^a_{bc}(\bar{x}) = 0, \quad \forall \, \bar{x}, \, a, \, b, \, c.$$

(5)

The coordinate system $\bar{x}^a$ exists if

$$\Gamma^a_{bd,c} - \Gamma^a_{bc,d} + \Gamma^a_{ec}\Gamma^e_{bd} - \Gamma^a_{de}\Gamma^e_{bc} = 0$$

(6)

for the affine connection $\Gamma^a_{bc}(x)$. The left hand side of Eq. (6) is the Riemann tensor:

$$R^a_{bcd} = \Gamma^a_{bd,c} - \Gamma^a_{bc,d} + \Gamma^a_{ec}\Gamma^e_{bd} - \Gamma^a_{de}\Gamma^e_{bc}.$$

(7)

When $R^a_{bcd} = 0$ the metric is flat, since its derivatives are zero. If $K = R^a_{bcd}R^{bcd}_a > 0$ the metric has positive curvature. Sometimes it is said that the Riemann tensor represents the gravitational field, since it only vanishes in the absence of fields. On the contrary, the affine connection can be set locally to zero by a transformation of coordinates. This fact, however, only reflects the equivalence principle: the gravitational field can be suppressed in any locally free falling system. In other words, the tangent space to the manifold that represents space-time is always Minkowskian. To determine the mathematical object of the theory that represents the gravitational field we have to consider the weak field limit of Eqs. (1). When this is done we find that the gravitational potential is identified with the metric coefficient $g_{00} \approx \eta_{00} + h_{00}$ and the coupling constant κ is $-8\pi G/c^4$. If *the metric represents the gravitational potential*, then *the affine connection represents the strength of the field itself*. This is similar to what happens in electrodynamics, where the 4-vector A^a represents the electromagnetic potential and the tensor field $F^{ab} = \partial_a A_b - \partial_b A_a$ represents the strength of the electromagnetic field. *The Riemann tensor, on the other hand, being formed by derivatives of the affine connection, represents the rate of change, both in space and time, of the strength of the gravitational field*.

The source of the gravitational field in Eqs. (1), the tensor field T_{ab}, stands for the physical properties of material things. It represents the energy and momentum of all non-gravitational systems. In the case of a point mass M and assuming spherical symmetry, the solution of Eqs. (1) represents a Schwarzschild black hole.

The Schwarzschild solution for a static mass M can be written in spherical coordinates $(t,\ r,\ \theta,\ \phi)$ as:

$$ds^2 = \left(1 - \frac{2GM}{rc^2}\right) c^2 dt^2 - \left(1 - \frac{2GM}{rc^2}\right)^{-1} dr^2 - r^2(d\theta^2 + \sin^2\theta d\phi^2). \tag{8}$$

The metric given by Eq. (8) has some interesting properties. Let's assume that the mass M is concentrated at $r = 0$. There seems to be two singularities at which the metric diverges: one at $r = 0$ and the other at

$$r_S = \frac{2GM}{c^2}. \tag{9}$$

The length r_S is known as the *Schwarzschild radius* of the object of mass M. Usually, at normal densities, r_S is well inside the outer radius of the physical system, and the solution does not apply to the interior but only to the exterior of the object . For a point mass, the Schwarzschild radius is in the vacuum region and the entire space-time has the structure given by (8).

It is easy to see that strange things occur close to r_S. For instance, for the proper time we get:

$$d\tau = \left(1 - \frac{2GM}{rc^2}\right)^{1/2} dt, \tag{10}$$

or

$$dt = \left(1 - \frac{2GM}{rc^2}\right)^{-1/2} d\tau, \tag{11}$$

When $r \longrightarrow \infty$ both times agree, so t is interpreted as the proper time measure from an infinite distance. As the system with proper time τ approaches to r_S, dt tends to infinity according to Eq. (11). The object never reaches the Schwarzschild surface when seen by an infinitely distant observer. The closer the object is to the Schwarzschild radius, the slower it moves for the external observer.

A direct consequence of the difference introduced by gravity in the local time with respect to the time at infinity is that the radiation that escapes from a given $r > r_S$ will be redshifted when received by a distant and static observer. Since the frequency (and hence the energy) of the photon depend on the time interval, we can write, from Eq. (11):

$$\lambda_\infty = \left(1 - \frac{2GM}{rc^2}\right)^{-1/2} \lambda. \tag{12}$$

Since the redshift is:

$$z = \frac{\lambda_\infty - \lambda}{\lambda}, \tag{13}$$

then

$$1 + z = \left(1 - \frac{2GM}{rc^2}\right)^{-1/2}, \tag{14}$$

and we see that when $r \longrightarrow r_S$ the redshift becomes infinite. This means that a photon needs infinite energy to escape from inside the region determined by r_S. Events that occur

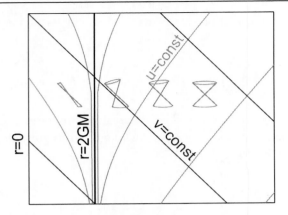

Figure 1. Space-time diagram in Eddington-Finkelstein coordinates showing the light cones close to and inside a black hole. Here, $r = 2GM = r_S$ is the Schwarzschild radius where the event horizon is located (units $c = 1$).

at $r < r_S$ are disconnected from the rest of the universe. The surface determined by $r = r_S$ is an *event horizon*. Whatever crosses the event horizon will never return. This is the origin of the expression "black hole", introduced by John A. Wheeler in the mid 1960s. The black hole is the region of space-time inside the event horizon.

According to Eq. (8), there is a divergence at $r = r_S$. The metric coefficients, however, can be made regular by a change of coordinates. For instance we can consider Eddington-Finkelstein coordinates. Let us define a new radial coordinate r_* such that radial null rays satisfy $d(ct \pm r_*) = 0$. Using Eq. (8) we can show that:

$$r_* = r + \frac{2GM}{c^2} \log \left| \frac{r - 2GM/c^2}{2GM/c^2} \right|.$$

Then, we introduce:

$$v = ct + r_*.$$

The new coordinate v can be used as a time coordinate replacing t in Eq. (8). This yields:

$$ds^2 = \left(1 - \frac{2GM}{rc^2} \right) (c^2 dt^2 - dr_*^2) - r^2 d\Omega^2$$

or

$$ds^2 = \left(1 - \frac{2GM}{rc^2} \right) dv^2 - 2dr dv - r^2 d\Omega^2, \tag{15}$$

where

$$d\Omega^2 = d\theta^2 + \sin^2 \theta d\phi^2.$$

Notice that in Eq. (15) the metric is non-singular at $r = 2GM/c^2$. The only real singularity is at $r = 0$, since there the Riemann tensor diverges. In order to plot the space-time in a (t, r)-plane, we can introduce a new time coordinate $t_* = v - r$. From the metric (15) or from Fig. 1 we see that the line $r = r_S$, $\theta =$constant, and $\phi =$ constant is a null ray, and hence, the surface at $r = r_S$ is a null surface. This null surface is an event horizon because inside $r = r_S$ all cones have $r = 0$ in their future (see Figure 1). Everything that crosses the event horizon will end at the singularity. This is the inescapable fate for everything inside a Schwarzschild black hole. There is no way to avoid it: in the future of every event inside the event horizon is the singularity. However, that no signal coming from the center of the black hole can reach a falling observer, since the singularity is always in the future, and a signal can arrive only from the past. A falling observer will never see the singularity.

Many coordinates systems can be used to describe black holes. For this reason, it is convenient to provide a definition of a black hole that is independent of the choice of coordinates. First, I will introduce some preliminary useful definitions (e.g., Hawking & Ellis 1973, Wald 1984).

Definition. *A causal curve in a space-time* (M, g_{ab}) *is a curve that is non space-like, that is, piecewise either time-like or null (light-like).*

We say that a given space-time (M, g_{ab}) is *time-orientable* if we can define over M a smooth non-vanishing time-like vector field.

Definition. *If* (M, g_{ab}) *is a time-orientable space-time, then* $\forall p \in M$, *the causal future of* p, *denoted* $J^+(p)$, *is defined by:*

$$J^+(p) \equiv \{q \in M | \exists \ a \ future - directed \ causal \ curve \ from \ p \ to \ q\}. \qquad (16)$$

Similarly,

Definition. *If* (M, g_{ab}) *is a time-orientable space-time, then* $\forall p \in M$, *the causal past of* p, *denoted* $J^-(p)$, *is defined by:*

$$J^-(p) \equiv \{q \in M | \exists \ a \ past - directed \ causal \ curve \ from \ p \ to \ q\}. \qquad (17)$$

The causal future and past of any set $S \subset M$ are given by:

$$J^+(S) = \bigcup_{p \in S} J^+(p) \qquad (18)$$

and,

$$J^-(S) = \bigcup_{p \in S} J^-(p). \qquad (19)$$

A set S is said *achronal* if no two points of S are time-like related. A Cauchy surface is an achronal surface such that every non space-like curve in M crosses it once, and only once, S. A space-time (M, g_{ab}) is *globally hyperbolic* iff it admits a space-like hypersurface $S \subset M$ which is a Cauchy surface for M.

Causal relations are invariant under conformal transformations of the metric. In this way, the space-times (M, g_{ab}) and $(M, \widetilde{g}_{ab})$, where $\widetilde{g}_{ab} = \Omega^2 g_{ab}$, with Ω a non-zero C^r function, have the same causal structure.

Let us now consider a space-time where all null geodesics that start in a region $\mathcal{J}^-$ end at $\mathcal{J}^+$. Then, such a space-time, (M, g_{ab}), is said to contain a *black hole if M is not*

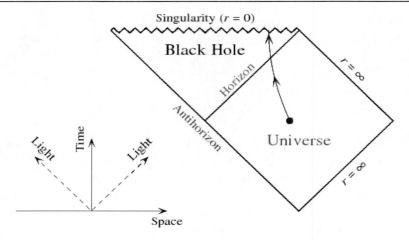

Figure 2. Carter-Penrose diagram of a Schwarzschild black hole.

contained in $J^-(\mathcal{J}^+)$. In other words, there is a region from where no null geodesic can reach the *asymptotic flat*[3] future space-time, or, equivalently, there is a region of M that is causally disconnected from the global future. The *black hole region*, BH, of such space-time is $BH = [M - J^-(\mathcal{J}^+)]$, and the boundary of BH in M, $H = J^-(\mathcal{J}^+) \bigcap M$, is the *event horizon* .

Notice that a black hole is conceived as a space-time *region*, i.e., what characterises the black hole is its metric and, consequently, its curvature. What is peculiar of this space-time region is that it is causally disconnected from the rest of the space-time: no events in this region can make any influence on events outside the region. Hence the name of the boundary, event horizon: events inside the black hole are separated from events in the global external future of space-time. The events in the black hole, nonetheless, as all events, are causally determined by past events. A black hole does not represent a breakdown of classical causality.

A useful representation of a black hole is given by a Carter-Penrose diagram. This is a two-dimensional diagram that captures the causal relations between different points in space-time. It is an extension of a Minkowski diagram where the vertical dimension represents time, and the horizontal dimension represents space, and slanted lines at an angle of 45° correspond to light rays. The main difference with a Minkowski diagram (light cone) is that, locally, the metric on a Carter-Penrose diagram is conformally equivalent[4] to the actual metric in space-time. The conformal factor is chosen such that the entire infinite space-time is transformed into a Carter-Penrose diagram of finite size. For spherically symmetric space-times, every point in the diagram corresponds to a 2-sphere. In Figure 2, I show a Carter-Penrose diagram of a Schwarzschild space-time.

---

[3]Asymptotic flatness is a property of the geometry of space-time which means that in appropriate coordinates, the limit of the metric at infinity approaches the metric of the flat (Minkowskian) space-time.

[4]I remind that two geometries are conformally equivalent if there exists a conformal transformation (an angle-preserving transformation) that maps one geometry to the other. More generally, two Riemannian metrics on a manifold M are conformally equivalent if one is obtained from the other through multiplication by a function on M.

From the Carter-Penrose diagram, it is clear that there is no time-like curve that starting from the interior region of the black hole can reach the conformally flat future infinity. All curves in this region can only end in the singularity.

Schwarzschild black holes are spherically symmetric, non-rotating objects. All known astrophysical systems have some angular momentum. In particular, since black holes of stellar mass are expected to result from the collapse of massive stars, they should be rapidly rotating objects due to the momentum conservation. The metric of a rotating mass in vacuum is the Kerr metric. For a rotating body of mass M and angular momentum per unit mass a, this metric can be written as:

$$ds^2 \quad = \quad g_{tt}dt^2 + 2g_{t\phi}dtd\phi - g_{\phi\phi}d\phi^2 - \Sigma\Delta^{-1}dr^2 - \Sigma d\theta^2 \tag{20}$$

$$g_{tt} \quad = \quad (c^2 - 2GMr\Sigma^{-1}) \tag{21}$$

$$g_{t\phi} \quad = \quad 2GMac^{-2}\Sigma^{-1}r\sin^2\theta \tag{22}$$

$$g_{\phi\phi} \quad = \quad [(r^2 + a^2c^{-2})^2 - a^2c^{-2}\Delta\sin^2\theta]\Sigma^{-1}\sin^2\theta \tag{23}$$

$$\Sigma \quad \equiv \quad r^2 + a^2c^{-2}\cos^2\theta \tag{24}$$

$$\Delta \quad \equiv \quad r^2 - 2GMc^{-2}r + a^2c^{-2}. \tag{25}$$

This is the Kerr metric in Boyer-Lindquist coordinates $(t, \ r, \ \theta, \ \phi)$. The metric reduces to the Schwarzschild metric for $a = 0$. In Boyer-Lindquist coordinates the metric is approximately Lorentzian at infinity.

The element $g_{t\phi}$ no longer vanishes. Even at infinity this element remains (hence I wrote *approximately* Lorentzian above). The Kerr parameter ac^{-1} has dimensions of length. The larger the ratio of this scale to GMc^{-2} (the *spin parameter* $a_* \equiv ac/GM$), the more aspherical the metric. Schwarzschild's black hole is the special case of Kerr's for $a = 0$. Notice that, with the adopted conventions, the angular momentum J is related to the parameter a by:

$$J = Ma. \tag{26}$$

Just as the Schwarzschild solution is the unique static vacuum solution of Eqs. (1) (a result called Israel's theorem), the Kerr metric is the unique stationary axisymmetric vacuum solution (Carter-Robinson theorem).

The horizon, the surface which cannot be crossed outwards, is determined by the condition $g_{rr} \to \infty$ ($\Delta = 0$). It lies at $r = r_{\mathrm{h}}^{\mathrm{out}}$ where

$$r_{\mathrm{h}}^{\mathrm{out}} \equiv GMc^{-2} + [(GMc^{-2})^2 - a^2c^{-2}]^{1/2}. \tag{27}$$

Indeed, the track $r = r_{\mathrm{h}}^{\mathrm{out}}$, $\theta = $ constant with $d\phi/d\tau = a(r_{\mathrm{h}}^2 + a^2)^{-1}\,dt/d\tau$ has $ds = 0$ (it represents a photon circling azimuthally *on* the horizon, as opposed to hovering at it). Hence the surface $r = r_{\mathrm{h}}^{\mathrm{out}}$ is tangent to the local light cone. Because of the square root in Eq. (27), the horizon is well defined only for $a_* = ac/GM \leq 1$. An *extreme* (i.e., maximally rotating) Kerr black hole has a spin parameter $a_* = 1$. Notice that for $(GMc^{-2})^2 - a^2c^{-2} > 0$ we have actually two horizons. The second, the *inner* horizon, is located at:

$$r_{\mathrm{h}}^{\mathrm{inn}} \equiv GMc^{-2} - [(GMc^{-2})^2 - a^2c^{-2}]^{1/2}. \tag{28}$$

This horizon is not seen by an external observer, but it hides the singularity to any observer that has already crossed r_h and is separated from the rest of the universe. For $a = 0$,

$r_{\mathrm{h}}^{\mathrm{inn}} = 0$ and $r_{\mathrm{h}}^{\mathrm{out}} = r_{\mathrm{S}}$. The case $(GMc^{-2})^2 - a^2c^{-2} < 0$ corresponds to no horizons and it is thought to be unphysical.

If a particle initially falls radially with no angular momentum from infinity to the black hole, it gains angular motion during the infall. The angular velocity as seen from a distant observer is:

$$\Omega(r,\ \theta) = \frac{d\phi}{dt} = \frac{(2GM/c^2)ar}{(r^2 + a^2c^{-2})^2 - a^2c^{-2}\Delta \sin^2 \theta}. \tag{29}$$

A particle falling into the black hole from infinite will acquire angular velocity in the direction of the spin of the black hole. As the black hole is approached, the particle will find an increasing tendency to get carried away in the same sense in which the black hole is rotating. To keep the particle stationary with respect to the distant stars, it will be necessary to apply a force against this tendency. The closer the particle will be to the black hole, the stronger the force. At a point r_{e} it becomes impossible to counteract the rotational sweeping force. The particle is in a kind of space-time maelstrom. The surface determined by r_{e} is the *static limit*: from there in, you cannot avoid to rotate. Space-time is rotating here in such a way that you cannot do anything in order to not co-rotate with it. You can still escape from the black hole, since the outer event horizon has not been crossed, but rotation is inescapable. The region between the static limit and the event horizon is called the *ergosphere*. The ergosphere is not spherical but its shape changes with the latitude θ. It can be determined through the condition $g_{tt} = 0$. If we consider a stationary particle, $r =$ constant, $\theta =$ constant, and $\phi =$ constant. Then:

$$c^2 = g_{tt}\left(\frac{dt}{d\tau}\right)^2. \tag{30}$$

When $g_{tt} \leq 0$ this condition cannot be fulfilled, and hence a massive particle cannot be stationary inside the surface defined by $g_{tt} = 0$. For photons, since $ds = cd\tau = 0$, the condition is satisfied at the surface. Solving $g_{tt} = 0$ we obtain the shape of the ergosphere:

$$r_{\mathrm{e}} = \frac{GM}{c^2} + \frac{1}{c^2}\left(G^2M^2 - a^2c^2\cos^2 \theta\right)^{1/2}. \tag{31}$$

The static limit lies outside the horizon except at the poles where both surfaces coincide. The phenomenon of "frame dragging'" is common to all axially symmetric metrics with $d_{t\phi} \neq 0$.

An essential singularity occurs when $g_{tt} \to \infty$. This happens if $\Sigma = 0$. This condition implies:

$$r^2 + a^2c^{-2}\cos^2 \theta = 0. \tag{32}$$

Such a condition is fulfilled only by $r = 0$ and $\theta = \frac{\pi}{2}$. This translates in Cartesian coordinates to[5]:

$$x^2 + y^2 = a^2c^{-2} \quad \text{and} \quad z = 0. \tag{33}$$

The singularity is a ring of radius ac^{-1} on the equatorial plane. If $a = 0$, then Schwarzschild's point-like singularity is recovered. If $a \neq 0$ the singularity is not necessarily in the future of all events at $r < r_{\mathrm{h}}^{\mathrm{inn}}$: the singularity can be avoided by some geodesics.

---

[5]The relation with Boyer-Lindquist coordinates is $x = \sqrt{r^2 + a^2c^{-2}}\sin\theta\cos\phi$, $y = \sqrt{r^2 + a^2c^{-2}}\sin\theta\sin\phi$, $z = r\cos\theta$.

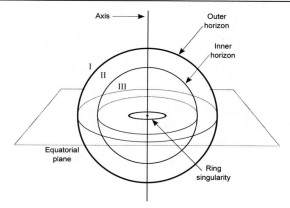

Figure 3. Sketch of a Kerr black hole, with its two horizons and the ring singulatrity.

A sketch of a Kerr black hole is shown in Figure 3.

Non-vacuum solutions of both spherically symmetric and rotating black holes exists, but since they are thought to be of no astrophysical importance, I do not discuss them here (the interested reader can see Romero & Vila 2014 and Punsly 2001).

3. Determinism and Predictability in Black Hole Spacetimes

Determinism is a metaphysical doctrine about the nature of the world. It is an ontological assumption: the assumption that all events are given. It can be traced to Parmenides and his "what is, is" (Romero 2012). It is important to emphasise that determinism does not require causality and does not imply predictability. Predictability is a property of our theories about the world, not a property of the world itself.

The confusion between determinism and predictability can be traced to Pierre-Simon Laplace and his *Philosophical Essay on Probabilities* :

> We may regard the present state of the Universe as the effect of its past and the cause of its future. An intellect which at a certain moment would know all forces that set nature in motion, and all positions of all items of which nature is composed, if this intellect were also vast enough to submit these data to analysis, it would embrace in a single formula the movements of the greatest bodies of the Universe and those of the tiniest atom; for such an intellect nothing would be uncertain and the future just like the past would be present before its eyes.

According to Laplace, every state of the Universe is determined by a set of initial conditions and the laws of physics. Since the laws are represented by differential equations and there are theorems for the existence and uniqueness of solutions, determinism implies predictability. Theorems apply, however, only to mathematical objects, not to reality. The world is not mathematical, just some of our representations of it are mathematical. The existence of solutions to some equations that represent physical laws does not imply physical

existence. Physical existence is independent of our conceptions. Moreover, even in Newtonian space-times there are Cauchy horizons (Earman 1986). These are hypersurfaces from
where, even the in case of a complete specification of initial data, the solutions of dynamical
equations cannot predict all future events. This arises because of the absence of an upper
bound on the velocities of moving objects in the Newtonian physics. For instance, consider
the trajectory of an object that is accelerated in such a way that its velocity becomes in
effect infinite in a finite time. This object will be disconnected from all later times.

General Relativity assumes the existence of all events represented by a manifold (see
the axiomatic system presented in Section 2). Hence, it is a deterministic theory from
an ontological point of view. The Cauchy problem, however, cannot always be solved in
General Relativity. Cauchy horizons naturally appear in many solutions of Einstein field
equations, and in particular, in those of rotating black holes. The inner horizons of both
Kerr and Kerr-Newman black holes are Cauchy surfaces: it is impossible to predict the
evolution of any physical system in the interior region from the specification of the initial
conditions over the horizon and the Einstein equations. Although the manifold is fixed, we
cannot always describe it from limited knowledge. General Relativity is an example of a
physical theory that can be ontologically deterministic but nonetheless epistemologically
underdetermined.

I remark that the existence of singular space-time models

$$M_{\mathrm{ST}}^{\mathrm{sing}} = \langle E, g_{ab}, T_{ab} \rangle$$

does not imply a breakdown of the ontological determinacy of the theory. Singularities,
certainly, imply a failure in the predictability, but they are not elements of space-time itself.
I will elaborate more about this in Section 7

The fact that there exist irreversible processes in the universe implies that space-time is
globally asymmetric. The laws that constrain the space-state of physical things, and therefore their potential to change, however, are invariant under time reversal. Black holes might
play a crucial role to link the the global structure of space-time with the local irreversibility
expressed by the Second Law of Thermodynamics. I turn now to this problem.

4.   Black Holes and the Second Law of Thermodynamics

The Second Law of Thermodynamics states that *the entropy of a closed system never decreases*. If entropy is denoted by S, this law reads:

$$\frac{dS}{dt} \geq 0. \tag{34}$$

In the 1870s, Ludwig Boltzmann argued that the effect of randomly moving gas
molecules is to ensure that the entropy of a gas would increase, until it reaches its maximum possible value. This is his famous *H-theorem*. Boltzmann was able to show that
macroscopic distributions of great inhomogeneity (i.e., of high order or low entropy) are
formed from relatively few microstate arrangements of molecules, and were, consequently,
relatively improbable. Since physical systems do not tend to go into states that are less
probable than the states they are in, it follows that any system would evolve toward the

macrostate that is consistent with the larger number of microstates. The number of microstates and the entropy of the system are related by the fundamental formula:

$$S = k \ln W, \tag{35}$$

where $k = 10^{-23}$ JK^{-1} is Boltzmann's constant and W is the volume of the phase-space that corresponds to the macrostate of entropy S.

More than twenty years after the publication of Boltzmann's fundamental papers on kinetic theory, it was pointed out by Burbury (1894, 1895) that the source of asymmetry in the H-theorem is the implicit assumption that the motions of the gas molecules are independent before they collide and not afterwards. This essentially means that the entropy increase is a consequence of the *initial conditions* imposed upon the state of the system. Boltzmann's response was:

> There must then be in the universe, which is in thermal equilibrium as a whole and therefore dead, here and there, relatively small regions of the size of our world, which during the relatively short time of eons deviate significantly from thermal equilibrium. Among these worlds the state probability increases as often as it decreases.

> Boltzmann (1895).

As noted by Price (2004): "The low-entropy condition of our region seems to be associated entirely with a low-energy condition in our past."

The probability of the large fluctuations required for the formation of the universe we see, on other hand, seems to be zero, as noted long ago by Eddington (1931): "A universe containing mathematical physicists at any assigned date will be in the state of maximum disorganisation which is not inconsistent with the existence of such creatures." Large fluctuations are rare ($P \sim \exp{-\Delta S}$); *extremely* large fluctuation, basically impossible. For the whole universe, $\Delta S \sim 10^{104}$ in units of $k = 1$. This yields $P = 0$.

In 1876, a former teacher of Boltzmann and later colleague at the University of Vienna, J. Loschmidt, noted:

> Obviously, in every arbitrary system the course of events must become retrograde when the velocities of all its elements are reversed.

> Loschmidt (1876).

In modern terminology, the laws of (Hamiltonian) mechanics are such that for every solution one can construct another solution by reversing all velocities and replacing t by $-t$. Since the Boltzmann's function $H[f]$ is invariant under velocity reversal, it follows that if $H[f]$ decreases for the first solution, it will increase for the second. Accordingly, the reversibility objection is that the H-theorem cannot be a general theorem for all mechanical evolutions of the gas. More generally, the problem goes far beyond classical mechanics and encompasses our whole representation of the physical world. This is because *all formal representations of all fundamental laws of physics are invariant under the operation of time reversal*. Nonetheless, the evolution of all physical processes in the universe is irreversible.

If we accept, as mentioned, that the origin of the irreversibility is not in the laws but in the initial conditions of the laws, two additional problems emerge: 1) What were exactly these initial conditions?, and 2) How the initial conditions, of global nature, can enforce, at any time and any place, the observed local irreversibility?

The first problem is, in turn, related to the following one, once the cosmological setting is taken into account: in the past, the universe was hotter and at some point matter and radiation were in thermal equilibrium; how is this compatible with the fact that entropy has ever been increasing according to the so-called Past Hypothesis, i.e., entropy was at a minimum at some past time and has been increasing ever since?

The standard answer to this question invokes the expansion of the universe: as the universe expanded, the maximum possible entropy increased with the size of the universe, but the actual entropy was left well behind the permitted maximum. The source of irreversibility in the Second Law of Thermodynamics is the trend of the entropy to reach the permitted maximum. According to this view, the universe actually began in a state of maximum entropy, but due to the expansion, it was still possible for the entropy to continue growing.

The main problem with this line of thought is that is not true that the universe was in a state of maximum disorder at some early time. In fact, although locally matter and radiation might have been in thermal equilibrium, this situation occurred in a regime were the global effects of gravity cannot be ignored (Penrose 1979). Since gravity is an attractive force, and the universe was extremely smooth (i.e structureless) in early times, as indicated, for instance, by the measurements of the cosmic microwave background radiation, the gravitational field should have been quite far from equilibrium, with very low global entropy (Penrose 1979). It seems, then, that the early universe was *globally* out of the equilibrium, being the total entropy dominated by the entropy of the gravitational field. If we denote by C^2 a scalar formed out by contractions of the Weyl tensor, the initial condition $C^2 \sim 0$ is required if entropy is still growing today [6].

The answer to the second question posed above, namely, 'how the Second Law is locally enforced by the initial conditions, which are of global nature?', seems to require a coupling between gravitation (of global nature) and electrodynamics (of local action). In what follows I suggest that black holes can provide the key for this coupling (for the role of cosmological horizons in this problem see Romero & Pérez 2011).

The electromagnetic radiation field can be described in the terms of the 4-potential A^μ, which in the Lorentz gauge satisfies:

$$\partial^b \partial_b A^a(\vec{r},\ t) = 4\pi j^a(\vec{r},\ t), \tag{36}$$

with $c = 1$ and j^a the 4-current. The solution A^a is a functional of the sources j^a. The retarded and advanced solutions are:

$$A^a_{\text{ret}}(\vec{r},\ t) = \int_{V_{\text{ret}}} \frac{j^a\left(\vec{r},\ t - \left|\vec{r} - \vec{r'}\right|\right)}{\left|\vec{r} - \vec{r'}\right|} d^3\vec{r'} + \int_{\partial V_{\text{ret}}} \frac{j^a\left(\vec{r},\ t - \left|\vec{r} - \vec{r'}\right|\right)}{\left|\vec{r} - \vec{r'}\right|} d^3\vec{r'}, \tag{37}$$

---

[6]This is because the Weyl tensor provides a measure of the inhomogeneity of the gravitational field. See Romero, Thomas, & Pérez (2012) for estimates of the gravitational entropy of black holes based on the Weyl tensor.

$$A_{\text{adv}}^{a}(\vec{r},\,t) = \int_{V_{\text{adv}}} \frac{j^{a}\left(\vec{r},\,t + \left|\vec{r} - \vec{r'}\right|\right)}{\left|\vec{r} - \vec{r'}\right|} d^{3}\vec{r'} + \int_{\partial V_{\text{adv}}} \frac{j^{a}\left(\vec{r},\,t + \left|\vec{r} - \vec{r'}\right|\right)}{\left|\vec{r} - \vec{r'}\right|} d^{3}\vec{r'}. \quad (38)$$

The two functionals of $j^{a}(\vec{r},\,t)$ are related to one another by a time reversal transformation. The solution (37) is contributed by sources in the past of the space-time point $p(\vec{r},\,t)$ and the solution (38) by sources in the future of that point. The integrals in the second term on the right side are the surface integrals that give the contributions from i) sources outside of V and ii) source-free radiation. If V is the causal past and future, the surface integrals do not contribute.

The linear combinations of electromagnetic solutions are also solutions, since the equations are linear and the Principle of Superposition holds. It is usual to consider only the retarded potential as physical meaningful in order to estimate the electromagnetic field at $p(\vec{r},\,t)$: $F_{\text{ret}}^{ab} = \partial^{a} A_{\text{ret}}^{b} - \partial^{b} A_{\text{ret}}^{a}$. However, there seems to be no compelling reason for such a choice. We can adopt, for instance (in what follows I use a simplified notation),

$$A^{a}(\vec{r},\,t) = \frac{1}{2}\left(\int_{J^{+}} \text{adv} + \int_{J^{-}} \text{ret}\right) dV. \quad (39)$$

If the space-time is curved ($R^{abcd} R_{abcd} \neq 0$), the null cones that determine the causal structure will not be symmetric around the point $p\ (\vec{r},\,t)$. In particular, the presence of event horizons can make very different the contributions from both integrals.

Hawking's black hole area theorem (Hawking 1971) ensures that in a time-orientable space-time such that for all null vectors k^{a} holds $R_{ab}k^{a}k^{b} \geq 0$, the area of the event horizons of black holes either remains the same or increases with cosmic time. More precisely:

Theorem. Let $(M,\ g_{ab})$ be a time-orientable space-time such that $R_{ab}k^{a}k^{b} \geq 0$ for all null k^{a}. Let Σ_{1} and Σ_{2} be space-like Cauchy surfaces for the globally hyperbolic region of the space-time with $\Sigma_{2} \subset J^{+}(\Sigma_{1})$, and be $\mathcal{H}_{1} = H \bigcap \Sigma_{1}$, $\mathcal{H}_{2} = H \bigcap \Sigma_{2}$, where H denotes an event horizon. Then $\mathcal{H}_{2} \geq \mathcal{H}_{1}$.

The fact that astrophysical black holes are always immersed in the cosmic background radiation, whose temperature is much higher than the horizon temperature, implies that they always accrete and then, by the first law of black holes (Bardeen et al. 1973), $\mathcal{H}_{2} > \mathcal{H}_{1}$. The total area of black holes increases with cosmic time. The accretion should include not only photons but also charged particles. This means that the total number of charges in the past of any point $p(\vec{r},\,t)$ will be different from their number in the corresponding future. This creates a local asymmetry that can be related to the Second Law.

We can introduce a vector field L^{a} given by:

$$L^{a} = \left[\int_{J^{-}} \text{ret} - \int_{J^{+}} \text{adv}\right] dV \neq 0. \quad (40)$$

If $g_{ab}L^{a}T^{b} \neq 0$, with $T^{b} = (1, 0, 0, 0)$ there is a preferred direction for the Poynting flux in space-time. The Poynting flux is given by:

$$\vec{S} = 4\pi \vec{E} \times \vec{B} = (T_{\text{EM}}^{01}, T_{\text{EM}}^{02}, T_{\text{EM}}^{03}), \quad (41)$$

where $\vec{E}$ and $\vec{B}$ are the electric and magnetic fields and T_{EM}^{ab} is the electromagnetic energy-momentum tensor.

In a black hole interior the direction of the Poynting flux is toward the singularity. In an expanding, accelerating universe, it is in the global future direction. We see, then, that a time-like vector field, in a general space-time (M, g_{ab}), can be *anisotropic*. There is a global to local relation given by the Poynting flux as determined by the curvature of space-time that indicates the direction along which events occur. Physical processes, inside a black hole, have a different orientation from outside, and the causal structure of the world is determined by the dynamics of space-time and the initial conditions. Macroscopic irreversibility [7] and time anisotropy emerge from fundamental reversible laws.

There is an important corollary to these conclusions. Local observations about the direction of events can provide information about global features of space-time and the existence of horizons and singularities.

5. Time and Black Holes

Presentism is a metaphysical thesis about what there is. It can be expressed as (e.g., Crisp 2003):

> *Presentism*. It is always the case that, for every x, x is present.

The quantification in this scheme is unrestricted, it ranges over all existents. In order to render this definition meaningful, the presentist must provide a specification of the term 'present'. Crisp, in the cited paper, offers the following definition:

> *Present*. The mereological sum of all objects with null temporal distance.

The notion of temporal distance is defined loosely, but in such a way that it accords with common sense and the physical time interval between two events. From these definitions it follows that the present is a thing, not a concept. The present is the ontological aggregation of all present things. Hence, to say that 'x is present', actually means "x is part of the present".

The opposite thesis of presentism is eternalism, also called four-dimensionalism. Eternalists subscribe the existence of past and future objects. The temporal distance between these objects is non-zero. The name four-dimensionalism comes form the fact that in the eternalist view, objects are extended through time, and then they have a 4-dimensional volume, with 3 spatial dimensions and 1 time dimension. There are different versions of eternalism. The reader is referred to Rea (2003) and references therein for a discussion of eternalism.

I maintain that presentism is incompatible with the existence of black holes. Let us see briefly the argument, considering, for simplicity, Schwarzschild black holes (for details, see Romero & Pérez 2014).

---

[7]Notice that the electromagnetic flux is related with the macroscopic concept of temperature through the Stefan-Boltzmann law: $L = A\sigma_{\mathrm{SB}}T^4$, where σ_{SB} is the Stefan-Boltzmann constant.

The light cones in Schwarzschild space-time can be calculated from the metric (8) imposing the null condition $ds^2 = 0$. Then:

$$\frac{dr}{dt} = \pm \left(1 - \frac{2GM}{r} \right), \tag{42}$$

where I made $c = 1$. Notice that when $r \to \infty$, $dr/dt \to \pm 1$, as in Minkowski space-time. When $r \to 2GM$, $dr/dt \to 0$, and light moves along the surface $r = 2GM$. The horizon is therefore a *null surface*. For $r < 2GM$, the sign of the derivative is inverted. The inward region of $r = 2GM$ is time-like for any physical system that has crossed the boundary surface. As we approach to the horizon from the flat space-time region, the light cones become thinner and thinner indicating the restriction to the possible trajectories imposed by the increasing curvature. On the inner side of the horizon the local direction of time is 'inverted' in the sense that all null or time-like trajectories have in their future the singularity at the center of the black hole.

There is a very interesting consequence of all this: an observer on the horizon will have her present *along* the horizon. All events occurring on the horizon are simultaneous. The temporal distance from the observer at any point on the horizon to any event occurring on the horizon is zero (the observer is on a null surface $ds = 0$ so the proper time interval is necessarily zero[8]). If the black hole has existed during the whole history of the universe, all events on the horizon during such history (for example the emission of photons on the horizon by infalling matter) are *present* to any observer crossing the horizon. These events are certainly not all present to an observer outside the black hole. If the outer observer is a presentist, she surely will think that some of these events do not exist because they occurred or will occur either in the remote past or the remote future. But if we accept that what there is cannot depend on the reference frame adopted for the description of the events, it seems we have an argument against presentism here. Before going further into the ontological implications, let me clarify a few physical points.

I remark that the horizon 1) does not depend on the choice of the coordinate system adopted to describe the black hole, 2) the horizon is an absolute null surface, in the sense that this property is intrinsic and not frame-dependent, and 3) it is a non-singular surface (or 'well-behaved', i.e., space-time is regular on the horizon).

In a world described by special relativity, the only way to cross a null surface is by moving faster than the speed of light. As we have seen, this is not the case in a universe with black holes. We can then argue against presentism along the following lines.

Argument $A1$:

- $P1$: There are black holes in the universe.

- $P2$: Black holes are correctly described by General Relativity.

- $P3$: Black holes have closed null surfaces (horizons).

- Therefore, there are closed null surfaces in the universe.

---

[8]Notice that this can never occur in Minkowski space-time, since there only photons can exist on a null surface. The black hole horizon, a null surface, can be crossed, on the contrary, by massive particles.

Argument $A2$:

- $P4$: All events on a closed null surface are simultaneous with any event on the same surface.

- $P4i$: All events on the closed null surface are simultaneous with the birth of the black hole.

- $P5$: Some distant events are simultaneous with the birth of the black hole, but not with other events related to the black hole.

- Therefore, there are events that are simultaneous in one reference frame, and not in another.

Simultaneity is frame-dependent. Since what there exist cannot depend on the reference frame we use to describe it, we conclude that there are non-simultaneous events. Therefore, presentism is false.

Let us see which assumptions are open to criticism by the presentist.

An irreducible presentist might plainly reject $P1$. Although there is significant astronomical evidence supporting the existence of black holes (e.g., Camenzind 2007, Paredes 2009, Romero and Vila 2014), the very elusive nature of these objects still leaves room for some speculations like gravastars and other exotic compact objects. The price of rejecting $P1$, however, is very high: black holes are now a basic component of most mechanisms that explain extreme events in astrophysics, from quasars to the so-called gamma-ray bursts, from the formation of galaxies to the production of jets in binary systems. The presentist rejecting black holes should reformulate the bulk of contemporary high-energy astrophysics in terms of new mechanisms. In any case, $P1$ is susceptible of empirical validation through direct imagining of the super-massive black hole "shadow" in the center of our galaxy by sub-mm interferometric techniques in the next decade (e.g., Falcke et al. 2011). In the meanwhile, the cumulative case for the existence of black holes is overwhelming, and very few scientists would reject them on the basis of metaphysical considerations only.

The presentist might, instead, reject $P2$. After all, we *know* that General Relativity fails at the Planck scale. Why should it provide a correct description of black holes? The reason is that the horizon of a black hole is quite far from the region where the theory fails (the singularity). The distance, in the case of a Schwarzschild black hole, is r_S. For a black hole of 10 solar masses, as the one suspected to form part of the binary system Cygnus X-1, this means 30 km. And for the black hole in the center of the galaxy, about 12 million km. Any theory of gravitation must yield the same results as General Relativity at such distances. So, even if General Relativity is not the right theory for the classical gravitational field, the correct theory should predict the formation of black holes under the same conditions.

There is not much to do with $P4$, since it follows from the condition that defines the null surface: $ds = 0$[9]; similarly $P4i$ only specifies one of the events on the null surface. A presentist might refuse to identify 'the present' with a null surface. After all, in Minkowskian space-time or even in a globally time-orientable pseudo-Riemannian space-time the present is usually taken as the hyperplane perpendicular to the local time. But in space-times with

---

[9]$ds = cd\tau = 0 \rightarrow d\tau = 0$, where $d\tau$ is the proper temporal separation.

black holes, the horizon is not only a null surface; it is also a surface locally normal to the time direction. In a Minkowskian space-time the plane of the present is not coincident with a null surface. However, close to the event horizon of a black hole, things change, as indicated by Eq. (42). As we approach the horizon, the null surface matches the plane of the present. On the horizon, both surfaces are exactly coincident. A presentist rejecting the identification of the present with a *closed* null surface on an event horizon should abandon what is perhaps her most cherished belief: the identification of 'the present' with hypersurfaces that are normal to a local time-like direction.

The result mentioned above is not a consequence of any particular choice of coordinates but an intrinsic property of a black hole horizon. This statement can be easily proved. The symmetries of Schwarzschild space-time imply the existence of a preferred radial function, r, which serves as an affine parameter along both null directions. The gradient of this function, $r_a = \nabla_a r$ satisfies ($c = G = 1$):

$$r^a r_a = \left(1 - \frac{2M}{r}\right). \tag{43}$$

Thus, r^a is space-like for $r > 2M$, null for $r = 2M$, and time-like for $r < 2M$. The 3-surface given by $r = 2M$ is the horizon H of the black hole in Schwarzschild space-time. From Eq. (43) it follows that $r^a r_a = 0$ over H, and hence H is a null surface[10].

Premise $P5$, perhaps, looks more promising for a last line of presentist defence. It might be argued that events on the horizon are not simultaneous with any event in the external universe. They are, in a very precise sense, cut off from the universe, and hence cannot be simultaneous with any distant event. Let us work out a counterexample.

The so-called long gamma-ray bursts are thought to be the result of the implosion of a very massive and rapidly rotating star. The core of the star becomes a black hole, which accretes material from the remaining stellar crust. This produces a growth of the black hole mass and the ejection of matter from the magnetised central region in the form of relativistic jets (e.g., Woosely 1993). Approximately, one of these events occur in the universe per day. They are detected by satellites like *Swift* (e.g., Piran and Fan 2007), with durations of a few tens of seconds. This is the time that takes for the black hole to swallow the collapsing star. Let us consider a gamma-ray burst of, say, 10 seconds. Before these 10 seconds, the black hole did not exist for a distant observer $O1$. Afterwards, there is a black hole

---

[10] An interesting case is Schwarzschild space-time in the so-called Painlevé-Gullstrand coordinates. In these coordinates the interval reads:

$$ds^2 = dT^2 - \left(dr + \sqrt{\frac{2M}{r}}\, dT\right)^2 - r^2 d\Omega^2, \tag{44}$$

with

$$T = t + 4M\left(\sqrt{\frac{2M}{r}} + \frac{1}{2}\ln\left|\frac{\sqrt{\frac{2M}{r}} - 1}{\sqrt{\frac{2M}{r}} + 1}\right|\right). \tag{45}$$

If a presentist makes the choice of identifying the present with the surfaces of $T =$ constant, from Eq. (44): $ds^2 = -dr^2 - r^2 d\Omega^2$. Notice that for $r = 2M$ this is the event horizon, which in turn, is a null surface. Hence, with such a choice, the presentist is considering that the event horizon is the hypersurface of the present, for all values of T. This choice of coordinates makes particularly clear that the usual presentist approach to define the present in general relativity self-defeats her position if space-time allows for black holes.

in the universe that will last more than the life span of any human observer. Let us now consider an observer $O2$ collapsing with the star. At some instant she will cross the null surface of the horizon. This will occur within the 10 seconds that the collapse lasts for $O1$. But for $O2$ all photons that cross the horizon are simultaneous, including those that left $O1$ long after the 10 seconds of the event and crossed the horizon after traveling a long way. For instance, photons leaving the planet of $O1$ one million years after the gamma-ray burst, might cross the horizon, and then can interact with $O2$. So, the formation of the black hole is simultaneous with events in $O1$ and $O2$, but these very same events of $O2$ are simultaneous with events that are in the distant future of $O1$.

The reader used to work with Schwarzschild coordinates perhaps will object that $O2$ never reaches the horizon, since the approaching process takes an infinite time in a distant reference frame. This is, however, an effect of the choice of the coordinate system and the test-particle approximation (see, for instance, Hoyng 2006, p.116). If the process is represented in Eddington-Finkelstein coordinates, it takes a finite time for the whole star to disappear, as shown by the fact that the gamma-ray burst are quite short events. Accretion/ejection processes, well-documented in active galactic nuclei and microquasars (e.g., Mirabel et al. 1998) also show that the time taken to reach the horizon is finite in the asymptotically flat region of space-time.

My conclusion is that black holes can be used to show that presentism provides a defective picture of the ontological substratum of the world.

6. Black Holes and Information

Black holes are often invoked in philosophical (and even physical) discussions about production and destruction of 'information'. This mostly occurs in relation to the possibility hypercomputing and the application of quantum field theory to the near horizon region. I shall review both topics here.

The expression 'hypercomputing' refers to the actual performance of an infinite number of operations in a finite time with the aim of calculating beyond the Turing barrier (Turing, 1936. For a definition of a Turing machine see Hopcrof & Ullman 1979). It has been suggested that such a hypercomputation can be performed in a Kerr space-time (Németi & David 2006, Németi & Handréka 2006). The Kerr space-time belongs to the class of the so-called Malament-Hogarth (M-H) space-times. These are defined as follows (Hogarth 1994):

Definition. (M, g_{ab}) *is an M-H space-time if there is a future-directed time-likehalf-curve* $\gamma \subset M$ *and a point* $p \in M$ *such that* $\int_\gamma d\tau = \infty$ *and* $\gamma \subset J^-(p)$.

The curve γ represents the world-line of some physical system. Because γ has infinite proper time, it may complete an infinite number of tasks. But, at every pointin γ, it is possible to send a signal to the point p. This is because there always exists a curve γ' with future endpoint p which has finite proper time. We can think of γ as the "sender" and γ' as the "receiver" of a signal. In this way, the receiver may obtain knowledge of the result of an infinite number of tasks in a finite time. In a Kerr space-time this scheme can be arranged as follows. The "sender" is a spacecraft orbiting the Kerr black hole with a computer onboard. The "receiver" is a capsule ejected by the orbiter that falls into the black hole. As the capsule approaches the inner horizon it intersects more and more signals from the orbiter, which emits periodically results of the computer calculations into the black hole. By the time the capsule crosses the inner horizon it has received all signals emitted by the computer in an infinite time (assuming that both the black hole and the orbiter can exist forever). This would allow the astronauts in the capsule to get answers to questions that require beyond-Turing computation! (Németi & David 2006). The whole situation is depicted in Figure 4.

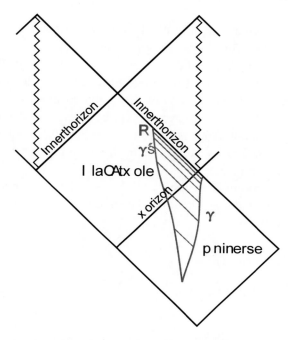

Figure 4. Carter-Penrose diagram of a Kerr black hole. The trajectories of two physical systems are indicated: γ remains in the exterior space-time for an infinite amount of time, whereas γ' falls into the black hole. In the time it takes the latter to reach the inner horizon, the former arrives to the conformal infinity. The lines that connect both trajectories represent signals sent from γ to γ'.

There are many reasons to think that the described situation is physically impossible. I shall mention the following ones: 1) The required inner black hole structure does not correspond to an astrophysical black hole generated by gravitational collapse. In a real black hole the Cauchy horizon is expected to collapse into a (probably null) singularity due to the backscattered gravitational wave tails that enter the black hole and are blueshifted at the Cauchy horizon (see next section and Brady 1999). The instability of the Cauchy horizon seems to be a quite general feature of any realistic black hole interior model. 2) The black hole is not expected to exist during an infinite duration: it should evaporate through Hawking radiation, over very long (but always finite) time. 3) The performance of infinite operations would require an infinite amount of energy (Bunge 1977, Romero 2014). Even if the universe were infinite, a finite spacecraft cannot manipulate infinite amounts of energy. 4) If signals are periodically sent to the receiver, the blushifted electromagnetic radiation would burn the capsule by the time it crosses the Cauchy horizon. Németi & David (2006) argue that this might be circumvented by sending just one signal with the final result. This suggestion faces the problems of the actual infinite: for any moment there will always be a further moment, then, when the spaceship would send this signal? 5) The universe seems to be entering into a de Sitter phase, so particle horizons will appear and block part of the accessible space-time to the spacecraft limiting its resources.

I think that the cumulative argument is strong enough to support a *hypercomputing avoidance conjeture*: the laws of physics are such that no actual hypercomputation can be performed.

I turn now to another issue related to black holes and information: the destruction of information by black holes. This seems to be a topic of high concern for quantum field theorists, to the point that the presumed destruction of information in a black hole is called the "black hole information paradox". I maintain that such a paradox does not exist: black holes cannot destroy any information. The reason is that information is not a property of physical systems. It is not like the electric charge, mass, or angular momentum. Information is an attribute of *languages*, and languages are constructs, i.e., elaborated fictions. To say that black holes can destroy information is like to say that they can destroy syntax. Let us review the situation in a bit more detail.

The application of quantum field theory to the near horizon region of a black hole results in the prediction of thermal radiation (Hawking 1974). A temperature, then, can be associated with the horizon:

$$T_{\text{BH}} = \frac{\hbar c^3}{8GMk} \cong 10^{-7}\text{K} \left(\frac{M_\odot}{M} \right).$$
(46)

We can write the entropy of the black hole as:

$$S = \int \frac{dQ}{T_{\text{BH}}} = \frac{kc^3}{4\pi\hbar G} A_{\text{BH}} + \text{ constant} \sim 10^{77} \left(\frac{M}{M_\odot} \right)^2 k \text{ JK}^{-1}.$$
(47)

The area of a Schwarzschild black hole is:

$$A_{\text{Schw}} = 4\pi r_{\text{Schw}}^2 = \frac{16\pi G^2 M^2}{c^4}.$$
(48)

In the case of a Kerr-Newman black hole, the area is:

$$
\begin{aligned}
A_{\text{KN}} &= 4\pi \left(r_+^2 + \frac{a^2}{c^2} \right) \\
&= 4\pi \left[\left(\frac{GM}{c^2} + \frac{1}{c^2}\sqrt{G^2M^2 - GQ^2 - a^2} \right)^2 + \frac{a^2}{c^2} \right].
\end{aligned}
$$
(49)

Notice that expression (49) reduces to (48) for $a = Q = 0$.

The formation of a black holes implies a huge increase of entropy. Just to compare, a star has an entropy ~ 20 orders of magnitude lower than the corresponding black hole of the same mass. This tremendous increase of entropy is related to the loss of all the structure of the original system (e.g., a star) once the black hole is formed.

The analogy between area and entropy allows to state a set of laws for black holes thermodynamics (Bardeen et al. 1973):

- First law (energy conservation): $dM = T_{BH}dS + \Omega_+ dJ + \Phi dQ + \delta M$. Here, Ω_+ is the angular velocity, J the angular momentum, Q the electric charge, Φ the electrostatic potential, and δM is the contribution to the change in the black hole mass due to the change in the external stationary matter distribution.

- Second law (entropy never decreases): In all physical processes involving black holes the total surface area of all the participating black holes can never decrease.

- Third law (Nernst's law): The temperature (surface gravity) of a black black hole cannot be zero. Since $T_{BH} = 0$ with $A \neq 0$ for extremal charged and extremal Kerr black holes, these are thought to be limit cases that cannot be reached in Nature.

- Zeroth law (thermal equilibrium): The surface gravity (temperature) is constant over the event horizon of a stationary axially symmetric black hole.

If a temperature can be associated with black holes, then they should radiate as any other body. The luminosity of a Schwarzschild black hole is:

$$L_{BH} = 4\pi r_{Schw}^2 \sigma T_{BH}^4 \sim \frac{16\pi\sigma\hbar^4 c^6}{(8\pi)^4 G^2 M^2 k^4}. \tag{50}$$

Here, σ is the Stephan-Boltzmann constant. This expression can be written as:

$$L_{BH} = 10^{-17} \left(\frac{M_\odot}{M}\right)^2 \quad \text{erg s}^{-1}. \tag{51}$$

The lifetime of a black hole is:

$$\tau \cong \frac{M}{dM/dt} \sim 2.5 \times 10^{63} \left(\frac{M}{M_\odot}\right)^3 \quad \text{years}. \tag{52}$$

Notice that the black hole heats up as it radiates! This occurs because when the hole radiates, its mass decreases and then according to Eq. (46) the temperature must rise. The black hole then will lose energy and its area will decrease slowly, violating the Second Law of Thermodynamics. However, there is no violation if we consider a *generalised second law*, that always holds: *In any process, the total generalised entropy $S + S_{BH}$ never decreases* (Bekenstein 1973).

Unfortunately, many physicists think that entropy and information are the same thing. This confusion seems to come from J. von Neumann, who advised, not without some sarcasm, Claude Shannon to adopt the expression 'entropy' to name the information characterised in the mathematical theory of communications developed by Shannon and Weaver (1949):

> You should call it entropy, for two reasons. In the first place your uncertainty function has been used in statistical mechanics under that name, so it already has a name. In the second place, and more important, nobody knows what entropy really is, so in a debate you will always have the advantage.

Floridi (2010), p. 46.

Shannon's information 'entropy', although formally defined by the same expression, is a much more general concept than statistical thermodynamic entropy. Information 'entropy' is present whenever there are unknown quantities that can be described only by a probability distribution. When some physicists write about a 'Principle of Information Conservation' (e.g., Susskind & Lindesay 2010), what they really mean is that the entropy of an isolated system in equilibrium should not increase, since it already is at its maximum value. When a black hole accretes matter, however, the entropy increases (they say that "information is destroyed"). Even if the black hole finally radiates away the whole mass absorbed, the radiation will be thermal, so the entropy of matter will continue to increase.

As pointed out by Penrose, these considerations do not take into account the entropy of the gravitational field. The state of maximum entropy of this field is gravitational collapse (Penrose 2010). As the black hole evaporates, the entropy of gravitation decreases. Eventually, after the black hole complete evaporation, radiation will be in thermal equilibrium and gravity in a maximally ordered state. After a huge amount of time, the universe might return to a state of minimum overall entropy. Black holes, in this sense, might act as some 'entropy regeneration engines', restoring the initial conditions of the universe.

There is yet another sense of the so-called black hole information paradox, related to the breakdown of predictability of quantum mechanics in presence of black holes. The paradox here appears because of a confusion between ontological and epistemic determinism (see Sect. 3 above). A fundamental postulate of quantum mechanics is that complete description of a system is given by its wave function up to when the system interacts. The evolution of the wave function is determined by a unitary operator, and unitarity implies epistemic determinism: initial and boundary conditions allow to solve the dynamic equation of the system and the solution is unique. If a system is entangled and one component cross the event horizon, measurements of the second component and knowledge of the initial state will, however, not allow to know the state of the component fallen into the black hole. Epistemic determinism fails for quantum mechanics in presence of black holes. I confess not to see a problem here, since quantum interactions are by themselves already non-unitary. Ontic determinism, the kind that counts, is not in peril here [11], and epistemic determinism was never part of a full theory of quantum mechanics.

7. Inside Black Holes

We have seen that black hole space-times are singular, at least in standard General Relativity. Moreover, singularity theorems formulated by Penrose (1965) and Hawking & Penrose (1970) show that this is an essential feature of black holes. Nevertheless, essential or true singularities should not be interpreted as representations of physical objects of infinite density, infinite pressure, etc. Since the singularities do not belong to the manifold that represents space-time in General Relativity, they simply cannot be described or represented in the framework of such a theory. General Relativity is incomplete in the sense that it cannot provide a full description of the gravitational behaviour of any physical system. True singularities are not within the range of values of the bound variables of the theory: they do not belong to the ontology of a world that can be described with 4-dimensional differential

---

[11] See Romero (2012, 2013a) on ontic determinism.

manifolds. Let us see this in more detail (for further discussions see Earman 1995).

A space-time model is said to be singular if the manifold E is *incomplete*. A manifold is incomplete if it contains at least one *inextendible* curve. A curve $\gamma : [0, a) \longrightarrow E$ is inextendible if there is no point p in E such that $\gamma(s) \longrightarrow p$ as $a \longrightarrow s$, i.e., γ has no endpoint in E. A given space-time model $\langle E, g_{ab} \rangle$ has an *extension* if there is an isometric embedding $\theta : M \longrightarrow E'$, where $\langle E', g'_{ab} \rangle$ is another space-time model and θ is an application onto a proper subset of E'. A *singular* space-time model contains a curve γ that is inextendible in the sense given above. Singular space-times are said to contain singularities, but this is an abuse of language: singularities are not 'things' in space-time, but a pathological feature of some solutions of the fundamental equations of the theory.

Singularity theorems can be proved from pure geometrical properties of the space-time model (Clarke 1993). The most important of these theorems is due to Hawking and Penrose (1970):

Theorem. Let $\langle E, g_{ab} \rangle$ be a time-oriented space-time satisfying the following conditions:

1. $R_{ab} V^a V^b \geq 0$ for any non space-like V^a[12].

2. Time-like and null generic conditions are fulfilled.

3. There are no closed time-like curves.

4. At least one of the following conditions holds

   - a. There exists a compact[13] achronal set[14] without edge.
   - b. There exists a trapped surface.
   - c. There is a $p \in E$ such that the expansion of the future (or past) directed null geodesics through p becomes negative along each of the geodesics.

Then, $\langle E, g_{ab} \rangle$ contains at least one incomplete time-like or null geodesic.

If the theorem has to be applied to the physical world, the hypothesis must be supported by empirical evidence. Condition 1 will be satisfied if the energy-momentum T^{ab} satisfies the so-called *strong energy condition*: $T_{ab} V^a V^b \geq -(1/2) T_a^a$, for any time-like vector V^a. If the energy-momentum is diagonal, the strong energy condition can be written as

---

[12]R_{ab} is the Ricci tensor obtained by contraction of the curvature tensor of the manifold E.

[13]A space is said to be compact if whenever one takes an infinite number of "steps" in the space, eventually one must get arbitrarily close to some other point of the space. Thus, whereas disks and spheres are compact, infinite lines and planes are not, nor is a disk or a sphere with a missing point. In the case of an infinite line or plane, one can set off making equal steps in any direction without approaching any point, so that neither space is compact. In the case of a disk or sphere with a missing point, one can move toward the missing point without approaching any point within the space. More formally, a topological space is compact if, whenever a collection of open sets covers the space, some sub-collection consisting only of finitely many open sets also covers the space. A topological space is called compact if each of its open covers has a finite sub-cover. Otherwise it is called non-compact. Compactness, when defined in this manner, often allows one to take information that is known locally – in a neighbourhood of each point of the space – and to extend it to information that holds globally throughout the space.

[14]A set of points in a space-time with no two points of the set having time-like separation.

$\rho + 3p \geq 0$ and $\rho + p \geq 0$, with ρ the energy density and p the pressure. Condition 2 requires that any time-like or null geodesic experiences a tidal force at some point in its history. Condition 4a requires that, at least at one time, the universe is closed and the compact slice that corresponds to such a time is not intersected more than once by a future directed time-like curve. The trapped surfaces mentioned in 4b refer to surfaces inside the horizons, from where congruences focus all light rays on the singularity. Condition 4c requires that the universe is collapsing in the past or the future.

I insist, the theorem is purely geometric, no physical law is invoked. Theorems of this type are a consequence of the gravitational focusing of congruences.

Singularity theorems are not theorems that imply physical existence, under some conditions, of space-time singularities. Material existence cannot be formally implied. Existence theorems imply that under certain assumptions there are functions that satisfy a given equation, or that some concepts can be formed in accordance with some explicit syntactic rules. Theorems of this kind state the possibilities and limits of some formal system or language. The conclusion of the theorems, although not obvious in many occasions, are always a necessary consequence of the assumptions made.

In the case of singularity theorems of classical field theories like General Relativity, what is implied is that under some assumptions the solutions of the equations of the theory are defective beyond repair. The correct interpretation of these theorems is that they point out the *incompleteness* of the theory: there are statements that cannot be made within the theory. In this sense (and only in this sense), the theorems are like Gödel's famous theorems of mathematical logic[15].

To interpret the singularity theorems as theorems about the existence of certain space-time models is wrong. Using elementary second order logic is trivial to show that there cannot be non-predicable objects (singularities) in the theory (Romero 2013b). If there were a non-predicable object in the theory,

$$(\exists x)_E \ (\forall P) \sim Px, \tag{53}$$

where the quantification over properties in unrestricted. The existential quantification $(\exists x)_E$, on the other hand, means

$$(\exists x)_E \equiv (\exists x) \wedge (x \in E).$$

Let us call P_1 the property '$x \in E$'. Then, formula (53) reads:

$$(\exists x)(\forall P)(\sim Px \wedge P_1 x), \tag{54}$$

which is a contradiction, i.e., it is false for any value of x.

I conclude that there are no singularities nor singular space-times. There is just a theory with a restricted range of applicability.

The reification of singularities can lead to accept an incredible ontology. We read, for instance, in a book on foundations of General Relativity:

---

[15]Gödel's incompleteness theorems are two theorems of mathematical logic that establish inherent limitations of all but the most trivial axiomatic systems capable of doing arithmetic. The first theorem states that any effectively generated theory capable of expressing elementary arithmetic cannot be both consistent and complete (Gödel 1931). The second incompleteness theorem, shows that within such a system, it cannot be demonstrated its own consistency.

[...] a physically realistic space-time *must* contain such singularities. [...] there exist causal, inextendible geodesics which are incomplete. [...] If a geodesic cannot be extended to a complete one (i.e., if its future endless continuation or its past endless continuation is of finite length), then either the particle suddenly ceases to exist or the particle suddenly springs into existence. In either case this can only happen if space-time admits a "singularity" at the end (or the beginning) of the history of the particle.

Kriele (1999), p. 383.

This statement and many similar ones found in the literature commit the elementary fallacy of confusing a model with the object being modelled. Space-time does not contain singularities. Some of our space-time models are singular. It is this incomplete character of the theory that prompt us to go beyond General Relativity in order to get a more comprehensive view of the gravitational phenomena. As it was very clear to Einstein, his general theory breaks down when the gravitational field of quantum objects starts to affect space-time.

Another interesting feature of black hole interiors is the existence, according to the unperturbed theory, of a region with closed time-like curves (CTCs) in Kerr and Kerr-Newman black holes. This is the region interior to the second horizon; chronology violation is generated by the tilt of the light cones around the rotation axis in this part of space-time (e.g., Andrka, Niémeti, & Wüthrich 2008). The interior event horizon is also a Cauchyhorizon – a null hypersurface which is the boundaryof the future domain of dependence for Cauchy dataof the collapse problem. It results impossible to predict the evolution of any system inside the Cauchy horizons; they are an indication of the breaking of predictability in the theory. These horizons, however, exhibit highlypathological behaviour; small time-dependent perturbationsoriginating outside the black hole undergo an infinitegravitational blueshift as they evolve towards the horizon. This blueshift of infalling radiationgave the first indications that these solutions maynot describe the generic internal structure of real black holes. Simpson & Penrose (1973)pointed this out more than 40 years ago, andsince then linear perturbations have been analysed in detail. Poisson & Israel (1990)showed that a scalar curvature singularity formsalong the Cauchy horizon of a charged, spherical black hole in asimplified model. This singularity is characterised bythe exponential divergence of the mass function with advancedtime. The key ingredient producing this growth of curvature is the blueshifted radiation fluxalong the inner horizon (see also Gnedin & Gnedin 1993 and Brady 1999 for a review). Since then, the result was generalised to Kerr black holes (e.g., Brady & Chambers 1996, Hamilton & Polhemus 2011). These, and other results about the instability of the Kerr black hole interior, suggest that CTCs actually do not occur inside astrophysical black holes.

8. Black Holes and the Future of the Universe

According to Eq. (52), an isolated black hole with $M = 10\ M_\odot$ would have a lifetime of more than 10^{66} yr. This is 56 orders of magnitude longer than the age of the universe. However, if the mass of the black hole is small, then it could evaporate within the Hubble time. A primordial black hole, created by extremely energetic collisions short after the Big Bang, should have a mass of at least 10^{15} g in order to exist today. Less massive black holes must have already evaporated. What happens when a black hole losses its mass so it cannot sustain an event horizon anymore? As the black hole evaporates, its temperature raises. When it is cold, it radiates low energy photons. When the temperature increases, more and more energetic particles will be emitted. At some point gamma rays would be produced. If there is a population of primordial black holes, their radiation should contribute to the diffuse gamma-ray background. This background seems to be dominated by the contribution of unresolved Active Galactic Nuclei and current observations indicate that if there were primordial black holes their mass density should be less than 10^{-8} Ω, where Ω is the cosmological density parameter ($\sim$ 1). After producing gamma rays, the mini black hole would produce leptons, quarks, and super-symmetric particles, if they exist. At the end, the black hole would have a quantum size and the final remnant will depend on the details of how gravity behaves at Planck scales. The final product might be a stable, microscopic object with a mass close to the Planck mass. Such particles might contribute to the dark matter present in the Galaxy and in other galaxies and clusters. The cross-section of black hole relics is extremely small: 10^{-66} cm^2 (Frolov and Novikov 1998), hence they would be basically non-interacting particles. A different possibility, advocated by Hawking (1974), is that, as a result of the evaporation nothing is left behind: all the energy is radiated.

Independently of the problem of mini black hole relics, it is clear that the fate of stellar-mass and supermassive black holes is related to fate of the whole universe. In an ever expanding universe or in an accelerating universe as it seems to be our actual universe, the fate of the black holes will depend on the acceleration rate. The local physics of the black hole is related to the cosmic expansion through the cosmological scale factor $a(t)$ (Faraoni & Jacques 2007). A Schwarzschild black hole embedded in a Friedmann-Lemaitre-Robertson-Walker (FLRW) universe can be represented by a generalisation of the McVittie metric (e.g., Gao et al. 2008):

$$ds^2 = \frac{\left[1 - \frac{2GM(t)}{a(t)c^2r}\right]^2}{\left[1 + \frac{2GM(t)}{a(t)c^2r}\right]^2}c^2dt^2 - a(t)^2\left[1 + \frac{2GM(t)}{a(t)c^2r}\right]^4(dr^2 + r^2d\Omega^2). \qquad (55)$$

Assuming that $M(t) = M_0 a(t)$, with M_0 a constant, the above metric can be used to study the evolution of the black hole as the universe expands. If the equation of state for the cosmic fluid is given by $P = \omega\rho c^2$, with ω constant, then for $\omega < -1$ the universe accelerates its expansion in such a way that the scale factor diverges in a finite time. This time is known as the Big Rip. If $\omega = -1.5$, then the Big Rip will occur in $\sim$ 35 Gyr. The event horizon of the black hole and the cosmic apparent horizon will coincide for some time $t < t_{\text{Rip}}$ and then the inner region of the black hole would be accesible to all observers. In case of $\omega > -1$ the expansion will continue during an infinite time. Black holes will become more and more isolated. As long as their temperature be higher than that of the Cosmic Microwave Background radiation (CMB), they will accrete photons and increase their mass. When, because of the expansion, the CMB temperature falls below that of the black holes, they will start to evaporate. On the very long run, all black holes will disappear. If massive particles decay into photons on such long timescales, the final state of the universe will be that of a dilute photon gas. Cosmic time will cease to make any sense for such a state of the universe, since whatever exist will be on a null surface. Without time, there will be nothing else to happen. Penrose (2010), however, has suggested that a countable sequence of open FLRW space-times, each representing a big bang followed by an infinite future expansion might occur, since the past conformal boundary of one copy of FLRW space-time can be "attached" to the future conformal boundary of another, after an appropriate conformal rescaling. Since bosons obey the laws of conformally invariant quantum theory, they will behave in the same way in the rescaled sections of the cyclical universe. For bosons, the boundary between different cycles is not a boundary at all, but just a space-like surface that can be passed across like any other. Fermions, on the other hand, remain confined to each cycle, where they are generated and decay. Most of the fermions might be converted into radiation in black holes. If this is correct, black holes would then be the key to the regeneration of the universe.

9.   Closing Remarks

In this chapter I have overviewed some philosophical problems related to black holes. The interface between black hole physics and philosophy remains mostly unexplored, and the list of topics I have selected is by no means exhaustive. The study of black holes can be a very powerful tool to shed light on many other philosophical issues in the philosophy of science and even in General Relativity. Evolving black holes, black hole dependence of the asymptotic behaviour of space-time, the nature of inertia, the energy of the gravitational field, quantum effects in the near horizon region, turbulent space-time during black hole mergers, the classical characterisation of the gravitational field, and regular black hole interiors are all physical topics that have philosophical significance. In black holes our current representations of space, time, and gravity are pushed to their very limits. The exploration of such limits can pave the way to new discoveries about the world and our ways of representing it. Discoveries in both science and philosophy.

Acknowledgments

I thank Mario Bunge, Daniela Pérez, Gabriela Vila, Federico Lopez Armengol, and Santiago Perez Bergliaffa for illuminating discussions on science and black holes. I am also very grateful to Florencia Vieyro for help with the figures. My work has been partially supported by the Argentinian Agency ANPCyT (PICT 2012-00878) and the Spanish MINECO under grant AYA2013-47447-C3-1-P.

References

[1] Andrka, H., Nmeti, I., & Wüthrich, C. 2008, *Class. Quantum Grav.*, 40, 1809-1823.

[2] Bardeen, J. M., Carter, B., & Hawking, S. W. 1973, *Communications in Mathematical Physics*, 31 (2), 161170.

[3] Bekenstein, J.D. 1973, *Phys. Rev. D*, 7, 2333-2346.

[4] Boltzmann, L. 1895, *Nature*, 51, 413-415.

[5] Brady, P.R., & Chambers, C.M. 1995, *Phys. Rev. D*, 51, 4177-4186.

[6] Brady, P.R. 1999, *Progress of Theoretical Physics Supplement*, 136, 29-44.

[7] Bunge, M. 1977, *Ontology I: The Furniture of the World*, Kluwer, Dordrecht.

[8] Burbury, S.H. 1894, *Nature*, 51, 78-79.

[9] Burbury, S.H. 1895, *Nature*, 51, 320-320.

[10] Camenzind, M. 2007, *Compact objects in Astrophysics: White Dwarfs, Neutron Stars and Black Holes*, Springer, Berlin.

[11] Crisp, T. 2003, Presentism. In: M. J. Loux & D. W. Zimmerman (Eds.), *The Oxford Handbook of Methaphysics*, pp. 211-245, Oxford University Press, Oxford.

[12] Earman, J., 1986, *A Primer on Determinism*, Reidel, Dordrecht.

[13] Earman, J., & Norton, J. 1993, *Philos. Sci.*, 60, 22-42.

[14] Earman, J., 1995, *Bangs, Crunches, Whimpers, and Shrieks: Singularities and Acausalities in Relativistic Spacetimes*, Oxford University Press, New York.

[15] Eddington, A.S. 1931, *Nature*, 127, 447-453.

[16] Falcke, H., Markoff S., Bower G. C., Gammie, C. F., Moscibrodzka, M. & Maitra, D. 2011. The Jet in the Galactic Center: An Ideal Laboratory for Magnetohydrodynamics and General Relativity. In: G. E. Romero, R. A. Sunyaev & T. Belloni (Eds.), *Jets at all Scales*, Proceedings of the International Astronomical Union, IAU Symposium, Volume 275, 68-76, Cambridge University Press, Cambridge.

[17] Faraoni, V., & Jacques, A. 2007, *Phys. Rev. D*, 76, id. 063510.

[18] Floridi, L. 2010, *Information.A Very Short Introduction*, Oxford University Press, Oxford.

[19] Frolov, V.P., & and Novikov, I.D. 1998, *Black Hole Physics*, Kluwer, Dordrecht.

[20] Gao, C., et al. 2008, *Phys. Rev. D*, 78, id. 024008.

[21] Gnedin, M. L., & Gnedin, N. Y. 1993, *Class. Quantum Grav.*, 10, 1083-1102.

[22] Gödel, K. 1931, *Monatshefte für Mathematik und Physik*, 38, 173-198.

[23] Hamilton, A.J.S., & Polhemus, G. 2011, *Phys. Rev. D*, 84, id. 124055.

[24] Hawking, S.W. 1971, *Physical Review Letters*, 26 (21), 13441346.

[25] Hawking, S.W. 1974, *Nature*, 248, 30-31.

[26] Hawking, S.W., and Ellis, G.F.R. 1973, *The Large-Scale Structure of Space-Time*, Cambridge University Press, Cambridge.

[27] Hopcroft, J., & Ullman, J. 1979, *Introduction to Automata Theory, Languages, and Computation* (1st ed.), AddisonWesley, Reading Mass.

[28] Hogarth, M. 1994, Non-Turing computers and non-Turing computability. In: Hull, D., Forbes, M., Burian,R. (Eds.), *Proceedings of the Biennial Meeting of the Philosophy of Science Association 1994*, pp. 126138, University of Chicago Press, Chicago.

[29] Hoyng, S. 2006, *Relativistic Astrophysics and Cosmology: A Primer*, Springer, Berlin.

[30] Kriele, M. 1999, *Spacetime: Foundations of General Relativity and Differential Geometry*, Springer, Berlin-Heidelberg-New York.

[31] Loschmidt, J. 1876, *Wiener Berichte*, 73, 128-142.

[32] Minkowski, H., 1908, Lecture "Raum und Zeit, 80th Versammlung Deutscher Naturforscher (Köln, 1908)", *Physikalische Zeitschrift*, 10, 75-88 (1909).

[33] Mirabel, I.F., Dhawan, V., Chaty, S., Rodriguez, L. F., Marti, J.,Robinson, C. R.,Swank, J., Geballe, T. 1998, *Astronomy & Astrophysics*, 330, L9-L12.

[34] Németi, I., & David, G. 2006, *Applied Mathematics and Computation*, 178, 118-142.

[35] Németi, I., & Andréka, H. 2006, New Physics and Hypercomputation. In: J. Wiedermann et al. (Eds.), *SOFSEM 2006*, LNCS 3831, p. 63, 2006.

[36] Paredes, J. M. 2009, Black Holes in the Galaxy. In: G. E. Romero & P. Benaglia (Eds.), *Compact Objects and their Emission*, Argentinian Astronomical Society Book Series, Volume 1, 91-121.

[37] Penrose, R. 1979, Singularities and Time-Asymmetry. In: S.W. Hawking & W. Israel (Eds.), *General Relativity: An Einstein Centennial*, Cambridge University Press, Cambridge, p.581, 1979.

[38] Penrose, R. 2010, *Cycles of Time*, Vintage Books, London.

[39] Piran, T. ,& Fan, Y. 2007, *Philosophical Transactions of the Royal Society A*, 365, 1151-1162.

[40] Poisson, E., & Israel, W. 1990, *Phys. Rev. D*, 41, 1796-1809.

[41] Price, H. 2004. In: *Contemporary Debates in Philosophy of Science*, C. Hitchcock (ed.), Blackwell, Singapore, p. 21.

[42] Punsly, B. 2001, *Black Hole Gravitohydromagnetics*, Springer, Berlin.

[43] Rea, M. C. 2003, Four-Dimensionalism. In: M. J. Loux & D. W. Zimmerman (Eds.), *The Oxford Handbook of Methaphysics*, pp. 246-80, Oxford University Press, Oxford.

[44] Romero, G.E. 2012, Foundations of Science, 17, 291-299.

[45] Romero, G.E. 2013a, *Foundations of Science*, 18, 139-148.

[46] Romero, G.E. 2013b, *Foundations of Science*, 18, 297-306.

[47] Romero, G.E. 2014a, *Foundations of Science*, 19, 209-216.

[48] Romero, G.E. 2014b, in M. Novello, S.E. Perez Bergliaffa, *Gravitation and Cosmology*, Cambridge, Cambridge Scientific Publishers, Ltd., in press.

[49] Romero, G.E., & Pérez, D. 2011, *Int. J. Modern Phys. D*, 20, 2831-2838.

[50] Romero, G. E., Thomas, R., & Pérez, D. 2012, *Int. J. Theor. Phys.*, 51, 925-942.

[51] Romero, G.E., & Vila, G.S. 2014, *Introduction to Black Hole Astrophysics*, Springer, Heidelberg.

[52] Romero, G.E., & Pérez, D. 2014, *European Journal for Philosophy of Science*, in press, DOI 10.1007/s13194-014-0085-6.

[53] Shannon, C.E., & Weaver, W. 1949, *The Mathematical Theory of Communications*, University of Illinois Press, Urbana Il.

[54] Simpson, M, & Penrose, R. 1973, *Int. J. Theor. Phys.*, 7, 183-197.

[55] Susskind, L., & Lindesay, J. 2010, *An Introduction to Black Holes, Information, and the String Theory Revolution*, World Scientific, Singapore.

[56] Turing, A. 1936, *Proceedings of the London Mathematical Society, Series 2*, 42, 230265.

[57] Wald, R.M. 1984, *General Relativity*, The University of Chicago Press, Chicago.

[58] Weingard, R. 1979, *Synthese*, 42, 191-219.

[59] Woosley, S. E. 1993, *ApJ*, 405, 273-277.

In: Advances in Black Holes Research
Editor: Abraham Barton

ISBN: 978-1-63463-168-6
© 2015 Nova Science Publishers, Inc.

Chapter 3

THE BLACK HOLE CHALLENGE IN RANDALL-SUNDRUM II MODEL

Nikolaos D. Pappas[*]

Department of Physics, National and Kapodistrian University of Athens,
Zografou University Campus, Athens, Greece

Abstract

Models postulating the existence of additional spacelike dimensions of macroscopic or even infinite size, while viewing our observable universe as merely a 3-brane living in a higher-dimensional bulk were a major breakthrough when proposed some 15 years ago. The most interesting among them both in terms of elegance of the setup and of the richness of the emerging phenomenology is the Randall-Sundrum II model where one infinite extra spacelike dimension is considered with an AdS topology, characterized by the warping effect caused by the presence of a negative cosmological constant in the bulk. A major drawback of this model is that despite numerous efforts no line element has been found so far that could describe a stable, regular, realistic black hole. Finding a smoothly behaved such solution supported by the presence of some more or less conventional fields either in the bulk and/or on the brane is the core of the black hole challenge. After a comprehensive presentation of the details of the model and the analysis of the significance and the utility of getting a specific analytic black hole solution, several (unsuccessful) analytic and numerical approaches to the problem developed over the years are presented with some discussion about their results. The chapter closes with the latest numerical results that actually consists a major advancement in the effort to address the challenge, the presentation of the most recent analytic work trying (and unfortunately failing) to build a solution assuming the existence of unconventional scalar fields and some ideas about the routes forthcoming analytic approaches should explore.

Introduction

Considering higher-dimensional spacetimes is not something new in Physics. Since the formulation of the General Theory of Relativity scientists have repeatedly developed models

---

[*] E-mail address: npappas@cc.uoi.gr.

where the key hypothesis was the existence of additional dimensions. After all, the tensorial nature of the foundations of the former and the concept of curved space-time manifold meant that the well understood mathematical tools, developed within the context of the 4-dimensional General Relativity, could be straightforwardly generalized to include extra dimensions, both spacelike and timelike ones, and trustworthily describe such spacetimes.

On one hand, higher-dimensional models have a very appealing aspect. Since they incorporate a greater freedom for the handling of the field equations, they can be (and have been) used as a basis to develop a more unified perception of Nature. That is to address distinct phenomena in our 4-dimensional world as different, low-energy, effective projections of the same higher-dimensional entity. This quality is, quite obviously, of tremendous importance in the quest for unification and ultimately for the long-pursued "Theory of Everything". The unification effectiveness of this approach has quite successfully manifested itself in the case of the 5-dimensional Kaluza - Klein model as well as in the framework of the 11-dimensional M-theory.

On the other hand, however, several serious-and-difficult-to-address issues rise when additional dimensions come into play. For example, the existence of an extra timelike dimension poses so many and so complicated causality challenges, that this kind of models rarely get even considered. Therefore, spacelike dimensions get all the attention. The main issue then has to do with the size and the geometry of the latter. If these extra dimensions are infinitely large, like the ordinary ones, why cannot we travel along or even see them? If, on the contrary, they are so small that we could only "see" them at not-yet-reached energies, one has to deal with the puzzle of possible mechanisms that have forced them not to expand like the other three ones we know of.

In the past 35 years or so Superstring Theory, being the most promising candidate for the Theory of Everything, while demanding the existence of several additional spacelike dimensions, inspired researchers to develop a multitude of higher-dimensional models in different directions. Among these models, up till recently, the too-small-to-be-observed approach was the dominant, if not the only, way scientists used to deal with the extra dimensions, the existence of which would provide them with the desired additional freedom for their models. Calabi - Yau manifolds are the most famous and characteristic representatives of this line of thinking.

However, in the turn of the last century, two novel theories were proposed, which tried to exploit the notion of branes and were grouped under the general title "brane world models". Branes (p-branes as a matter of fact) are structures that emerge in the frame of Superstring Theory and play a fundamental role in this context. They are extended objects of p spatial dimensions (strings for example are 1-branes) of whom the most important subgroup are the D-branes, on which open strings can end. Open strings describe the non-gravitational sector and their endpoints are firmly attached to branes. Closed strings, on the other hand, that describe the gravitational degrees of freedom, can propagate into the bulk. It comes quite naturally then to approach the observable Universe as a 3-brane, that is a (1+3)-hypersurface embedded in a (1+3+n)-dimensional space-time (the bulk), with Standard Model particles and fields trapped on the brane, while gravity is free to access the bulk. This is, in a nutshell, the central idea of the brane world models.

What was really innovative, though, was the fact that these models incorporated for the first time the idea of extra spacelike dimensions of macroscopic size. The first such model proposed back in 1998 [1] by N. Arkani-Hamed, S. Dimopoulos and G. Dvali (ADD) postulated the existence of an arbitrary number of additional spacelike dimensions of flat topology, transverse to our 4-dimensional brane, having a size up to several μm, based on the fact that the validity of the inverse-square law for gravity has only been experimentally checked (by Cavendish-type experiments) to this limit. The ADD model drew a great deal of attention since for the first time large extra dimensions were employed and predictions that could be actually get falsified through experiment were made. Even though there are some serious conceptual problems concerning the formulation of the model, one should always acknowledge that it was the one that brought in the foreground the hypothesis that extra dimensions could be significantly different than the compactified-to-Planck-scale ones, we used to consider up till then.

Shortly after the ADD scenario was proposed another brane world model was put forward by L. Randall and R. Sundrum [2]. Actually they managed to build two, related but different models with distinct merits and problems. The trademark of the RS-models is the rather radical assumption concerning the existence of one additional spacelike dimension of infinite size transverse to our brane. The extra dimension doesn't have the trivial flat topology, though. Instead, it is characterized by the presence of a negative bulk cosmological constant Λ_5, which causes spacetime to warp and acquire an ever increasing curvature, as we move away from the brane of reference. The bulk space-time, therefore, is an anti-de-Sitter one with ℓ, being its curvature radius related to Λ_5 as

$$\Lambda_5 = -\frac{6}{\ell^2}.$$

Another important property of the bulk is that Z_2-symmetry applies in it, which means that spacetime looks exactly the same when we move away from the brane by the same distance along the extra dimension, no matter to which direction we do so. The corresponding line-element is written as

$$ds^2 = e^{-2|y|/\ell}\eta_{\mu\nu}dx^\mu dx^\nu + dy^2, \tag{1}$$

with $\eta_{\mu\nu}$ being the Minkowski metric and the Z_2-symmetry being realized by the presence of the factor $|y|$ in the exponent. The term $e^{-2|y|/\ell}$, usually called the "warp factor", stems from the existence of Λ_5 in the bulk and is the reason why gravity remains largely confined near the brane even though gravitons can, in principle, propagate throughout the entire (infinite) extra dimension. The brane *per se* (located at $y = 0$) has a flat Minkowski topology and we ascribe a tension to it, that represents the brane self-gravity.

From the two RS models we shall focus our attention on the one known as RS-II or single-brane RS model, as it is not only simpler and geometrically appealing, but at the same time is proven to provide a framework for AdS/CFT correspondence, while presenting a more interesting phenomenology compared to the RS-I (or two-brane) model. The main result in this context is that even though the KK modes have a continuous spectrum, the impact of the $m \neq 0$ modes on the gravitational potential is quite small, because of the warp factor.

Furthermore, the massless mode (that can be seen as the massless graviton) "sees" a potential of the form

$$V(y) = \frac{15k^2}{8(k|y|+1)^2} - \frac{3k}{2}\delta(y),$$

(2)

where $k \equiv 1/\ell$, that forces it to remain localized closely around the brane, thus we can speak about a bound state mode (see Figure 1).

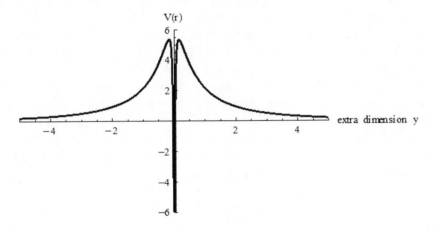

Figure 1. The "volcano" potential that causes the localization of the massless graviton in the frame of the RS-II model. The brane is located at y=0. The values on the axes mean nothing in particular as they depend on the details of the model. The important thing is the shape of the potential, which imposes this localization.

In this way the question why we don't detect the infinite extra dimension is addressed on the basis that in our low-energy experiments we deal only with the massless graviton, which is closely localized near our brane because of the warping effect of the bulk, so we have no way to directly interact with the fifth dimension in order to actually see it (remember that all other particles are strictly restricted on the brane by definition). At higher energies we would be able to study different graviton modes that would reveal the new dimension in question. The result of the aforementioned potential and the resulting confinement of the massless graviton near our brane is that the 4-dimensional gravitational potential on the latter is written as

$$V(r) \cong \frac{GM}{r}\left(1 - \frac{1}{r^2 k^2}\right)$$

(3)

The Importance of a Viable Black Hole Solution

The main motivation in the first place for the formulation of brane world models was the attempt to find a solution to the hierarchy problem, that is the huge discrepancy between the electroweak scale and the ordinary Planck scale, where quantum-gravitational effects arise, as observed in 4 dimensions. In such models the additional freedom that stems from the existence of extra dimensions, allows for some more radical approaches to the problem. In general, the two scales are assumed to be of the same order, while the hierarchy problem is seen as merely an artifact emerging on our brane, due to the non-trivial topology of the spacetime as a whole. Very soon, it became clear that their implications were much wider since the pioneering idea of an additional, warped and of infinite size spacelike dimension led to the reviewing of all known solutions and predictions of 4-dimensional gravity. Black-hole solutions were naturally subjected to this reviewing process as well. Interestingly enough, constructing a regular black hole metric in the context of Warped Extra Dimension Scenario proved to be a very difficult goal that is yet to be achieved. The lack of such solutions is not to be considered of secondary importance. The black hole criterion is chief among the theoretical ones that will eventually establish or refute the validity of the Warped Extra Dimension Scenario as a realistic prototype of the fundamental gravitational theory, capable of addressing long-standing problems of four-dimensional physics.

There are two very important reasons why so many scientists have engaged themselves in the research for a higher-dimensional black hole solution. The first one has to do with the possibility to employ the AdS/CFT duality in order to deal with hard-to-confront issues in four dimensions starting from a simpler and classical 5-dimensional picture. It is known that the classical dynamics of the AdS_5 gravitational background correspond to the quantum dynamics of a 4-dimansional conformal field on the brane at linear perturbative order at least [3]. In this context the RS-II model is dual with 4-dimensional General Relativity coupled to conformal fields and, consequently, a classical 5-dimensional black hole solution in this framework is in its turn dual with a quantum-corrected black hole in four dimensions. This last connection is very interesting since it means that the (hard to calculate) quantum driven backreaction due to Hawking radiation and higher order corrections to the latter in a 4-dimensional background can be equally well described as part of the (much easier, in principle, to handle) classical dynamics of the black hole in five dimensions. Needless to say that the deeper understanding of the evaporation process of black holes (being more or less the sole region where quantum mechanics and general relativity enter on an equal footing) can provide us with valuable insights regarding the mechanisms of the long pursued theory of Quantum Gravity and this perspective makes the quest for a higher-dimensional black hole solution both important and exciting.

The other one is the prospect that naturally emerges in the case of brane world models that the creation of black holes would become significantly easier and even possible at energies accessible by current experiments. Should this prediction gets verified by reality, we would witness the birth of microscopic black holes in some accelerator collision experiment, which shortly afterwards would evaporate through the emission of Hawking radiation almost instantly. Since all these phenomena would take place in front of our detectors in a well known and controlled environment, we will be able to fully detect and record this emission. As black holes are purely gravitational objects, their behavior is determined and affected by the overall spacetime geometry. Therefore, the details of the spectrum of the emitted degrees of freedom would then provide us with solid evidence concerning the true geometry of spacetime, the existence of additional dimensions as well as the size and the topology of the latter.

And here lies the catch. In order to make the calculations necessary to determine the exact connection between the properties of the Hawking radiation spectrum and the parameters of the spacetime geometry so as to evaluate any future detector signals, one has to know the metric describing the higher-dimensional black hole in question each time. In the

ADD scenario the study of black holes is straightforward since higher-dimensional (with extra dimensions being flat) versions of the Schwarzschild and Kerr solutions are known for decades (Schwarzschild-Tangherlini and Myers-Perry solutions respectively). However, in the much more interesting RS-II model (or Warped Extra Dimension Scenario) the task of deriving a black-hole solution localized on our brane (where the gravitational collapse of matter takes place), while embedded in a curved 5-dimensional background without any spacetime singularities appearing in an uncontrollable way has proven to be unexpectedly difficult.

Both analytic and numerical methods were (mostly unsuccessfully) employed to reach a solution. Even unsuccessful attempts, though, have offered valuable insights concerning the complications of the challenge and, therefore, a review of these efforts is very educative and moreover useful as basis for further research.

Analytical Approaches

In the very first attempt to derive such a brane-world black-hole solution Chamblin, Hawking and Reall replaced the Minkowski part $\eta_{\mu\nu}$ of the original RS-II metric (1) with the Schwarzschild line element producing the metric [4]

$$ds^2 = e^{2A(y)}\left[-\left(1-\frac{2M}{r}\right)dt^2 + \left(1-\frac{2M}{r}\right)^{-1}dr^2 + r^2(d\theta^2 + sin^2\theta\, d\varphi^2)\right] + dy^2$$

where the function $e^{2A(y)}$ is the generalized warping factor that can be reduced to the RS model one for $A(y) = -k\,|y|$, with k being the curvature radius of the AdS bulk spacetime. The metric succeeds in satisfying the corresponding 5-dimensional Einstein field equations. This should not be surprising since both Schwarzschild and Minkowski metrics are vacuum solutions of the field equations. Nevertheless, the aforementioned line element fails to describe a regular, localized on the brane black hole since it actually encompasses a linear singularity that extends throughout the infinite fifth dimension. The latter is clearly revealed when calculating the value of the invariant gravitational quantity $R^{MNP\Sigma}R_{MNP\Sigma}$. Then one finds

$$R^{MNRS}R_{MNRS} = \frac{48e^{-4A(y)}M^2}{r^6} + \cdots \tag{4}$$

It is obvious that for any warp function whose value reduces away from the brane (as in the RS-II case) the above quantity diverges as y goes to infinity. Even worse, equation (4) indicates the existence of a singularity at $r = 0$ for every slice of the 5-dimensional AdS spacetime related to a constant value of the y parameter. Therefore, the line element in question actually describes a black string rather than a black hole which ''escapes'' from the brane and extends up to the infinite boundaries of the fifth dimension contrary to the original motivation of the authors that proposed it. On top of that, shortly after it was shown that the black string is unstable because of the well-known from String Theory Gregory-Laflamme mechanism [5, 6].

Looking more carefully at the form of the metric one can safely infer that the emergence of the black string is related to the factorized nature of the former, which means that its 4-dimensional part *per se* has no dependence on the fifth dimension coordinate (apart of course from the fact that it is multiplied with the y-dependent warp factor). It is quite natural then to assume that the restriction of the extended singularity near the brane and the reestablishment of the spacetime smoothness at a relatively short distance away from the brane could be realized through the use of a non-factorized metric, where the 4-dimensional part, observed on the brane, has an explicit dependence on the additional dimension. The choice of the right metric to do the job is not an easy task though. Earlier studies have shown that non-factorized metrics, characterized by the existence of a horizon in their 4-dimensional section, lead to spacetimes where additional singularities emerge other than expected one in the black hole centre [7, 8]. However, the following modified 4-dimensional Vaidya-type metric embedded in a 5-dimensional spacetime with a warped extra dimension seemed that it could lead to a satisfying and viable solution

$$ ds^2 = e^{2A(y)} \left[-\left(1 - \frac{2m(u,y)}{r}\right) du^2 + 2\varepsilon du dr + r^2 (d\theta^2 + sin^2\theta d\varphi^2) \right] + dy^2 \tag{5} $$

First of all, being analytic in four dimensions the metric (5) is free of unexpected singularities. In addition to this the fact that the mass is a function of the extra dimension provides us, at least in principle, the opportunity to construct a modified, perturbed Schwarzschild-type solution in the context of which the singularity remains well-behaved and localized near the brane. Indeed, a mass function that decays faster than the square of the warp factor is capable of eliminating the singular term in the expression (4) of the curvature invariant quantity $R^{MNP\Sigma} R_{MNP\Sigma}$ within an acceptably short distance away from the brane. Despite the merits of the assumed metric, it was impossible to formulate a suitable, well-defined and functional modified version of the RS-II model that would produce a black hole solution with the desired properties. The reason is that the 4-dimensional on-brane projection of the metric (5) is no longer a vacuum solution therefore a non-trivial mass-energy distribution is necessary in order for the full 5-dimensional metric to satisfy the corresponding higher-dimensional field equations in the bulk. The functional form of the sought energy-momentum tensor was determined in [8] and was shown to satisfy all energy conditions on the brane. Furthermore, the distribution of the mass-energy related to this tensor along the extra dimension was found to have the shape of a shell which envelops the brane and thus is able to restrain the spacetime singularity of the black hole near it. Unfortunately, no self-consistent and acceptable field theory was possible to found that could give a physical explanation of this energy-momentum tensor.

The idea of bulk black holes interacting with or intersecting branes and to find the black hole features through the study of this interaction was considered in [9]-[12] and much more recently in [13]. The line element used by Creek, Gregory, Kanti and Mistry was the following [9]

$$ ds^2 = -U(r) dt^2 + U(r)^{-1} dr^2 + r^2 (d\chi^2 + sin^2\chi d\Omega_2^2) \tag{6} $$

with the function $U(r)$ equal to

$$U(r) = 1 + k^2 r^2 - \frac{\mu}{r^2}$$

The analysis was based on the use of suitably modified Israel junction conditions

$$[K_{\mu\nu} - K h_{\mu\nu}] = \kappa_5 T_{\mu\nu}$$

(with $K_{\mu\nu}$ the extrinsic curvature, $h_{\mu\nu}$ the on-brane projected metric and $T_{\mu\nu}$ the brane energy-momentum tensor, which was postulated - and hoped - to be that of a perfect fluid). From the junction conditions a set of differential equations was produced, where the trajectory of the brane $\chi(t,r)$, the brane energy density $\rho(t,r)$ and the brane equation of state $\omega(t,r)$ were the unknown parameters. Nevertheless, no parameter combination was able to produce a black hole solution with the desired properties.

A different approach was offered in [14] by Shiromizu, Maeda and Sasaki whose perspective was to incorporate the effects on the brane of the 5-dimensional Weyl tensor $C_{\mu\alpha\nu\beta}$ (see also [15]). The idea is that an observer on the brane is going to see only the part of the (generally unknown) Weyl tensor, that is projected on the brane, called the Weyl term $\in_{\mu\nu}$. Then the corresponding on-bane Einstein filed equations for the observer would be

$$G_{\mu\nu}^{(4)} = 8\pi G_4 T_{\mu\nu} + \kappa_5^4 \pi_{\mu\nu} + \in_{\mu\nu}$$

where the tensor $\pi_{\mu\nu}$ is quadratic with respect to the energy-momentum tensor $T_{\mu\nu}$ and consequently can safely be regarded as ignorable at the low-energy limit, where all on-brane measures are expected to take place. Furthermore, based on a series of assumptions concerning the possibility of decomposing the Weyl term into two independent parts, the relation between these parts and the asymptotic behavior of $\in_{\mu\nu}$ the authors managed to produce a brane black hole solution known as the tidal Reissner-Nordstrom solution (even though no electric charge is present). However, the tidal charge appearing in the solution stems from the existence of the on-brane mass since the latter is the source of the bulk Weyl field. So here lies a cyclic and ill-understood mechanism where the on-brane mass generates a gravitational field that gets reflected back on the brane through the higher-dimensional bulk. Interesting as it may be, the overall picture remains nonetheless obscure. In addition, there are still open questions regarding the applicability of the method in the case of large black holes, the emergence of "wormholes" and the exact expression of the Weyl term.

Apart from the aforementioned four basic approaches, there are also several other papers where issues related to the black hole challenge get analytically treated like [16]-[21].

Numerical Approaches

Since all efforts to find a closed-form analytic black hole solution failed in decisively addressing the challenge, numerical calculations were rather predictably the next major approach to the problem in order to provide evidence about the existence of such solutions, hints about the black hole properties and perhaps reveal the interaction between the overall spacetime geometry and the black hole behavior. Indeed, small brane-world black holes were shown to exist via numerical analysis possessing all the desired properties[1] [22]-[24] (even in this case, though, there were objections regarding the methods followed [25]). This kind of solutions, however, was possible to construct strictly when assuming that the black hole size is smaller than the characteristic curvature scale ℓ of the AdS spacetime. In this case the black hole is so small that "sees" all dimensions at an equal footing without really "feeling" the warping effect of the bulk, so that it can be approximated by a 5-dimensional Schwarzschild solution. When considering larger black holes with a horizon even the size of l no solution could be reached, let alone the case of realistic black holes. Nature, nevertheless, seems to work in much the opposite way: small black holes may have been indeed formed in the primordial universe but none has ever been observed. Large black holes, on the other hand, with masses a million times that of the sun and macroscopic size horizons, are today believed to inhabit the center of almost every galaxy. The General Theory of Relativity allows for the analytic determination of all black-hole solutions in 4 dimensions. If the fundamental theory of gravity is indeed higher-dimensional, with its geometrical set-up being similar to the Warped Extra Dimension Scenario, then, in principle, both small and large regular black-hole solutions should exist, thus numerical calculations should not indicate otherwise.

An interesting argument, related to the existence or not of static black hole solutions in the framework of warped spacetimes, comes from the AdS/CFT correspondence point of view [26]-[28]. The general idea is that in the 4-dimensional CFT picture (which is dual to the 5-dimensional AdS picture we engaged our study so far) a black hole co-exists with a large number of conformal fields. Larger number of degrees of freedom that can be emitted means that the Hawking radiation of the black hole should be significantly enhanced. Because of the augmented magnitude of the radiation the back-reaction on the metric of the black hole mass decrease can no longer be considered negligible, thus there is no ground for a static black hole to exist. Should this argument be valid, then static localized black holes of size larger than l (where the AdS/CFT duality holds) may not exist at all, in accordance to the results of the aforementioned numerical calculations.

In any case numerical analyses performed so far have reached non – conclusive and often contradictory results regarding realistic black hole solutions on the brane leading to arguments in favor [29]-[32] as well as against [33]-[38] their existence, only to confirm the profound difficulty of constructing such a solution already indicated by the failures of the analytic approaches mentioned earlier.

Latest News from the Front

Significant progress was made in 2011 by Figueras and Wiseman [39] who managed to develop a numerical code capable of describing both large and small stable black holes within the framework of the RS-II geometry. In addition, Abdolrahimi, Cattoen, Page and Yaghoobpour-Tari [40] following a different method (based on the AdS_5/CFT_4 duality as in the previous case) also managed to numerically produce large black hole solutions in the same background. Their findings renewed the interest of the scientific community on the

---

[1] That is to have a horizon at a distance from the singularity, their metric functions and derivatives to be finite (except of course at the singularity), while AdS5 geometry should be recovered at asymptotic infinity.

subject since it became evident that the elusive-up-to-now black hole solutions do exist, despite all the doubts and disappointments accumulated over the years.

In 2013 another attempt to analytically address the challenge was launched by Kanti, Pappas and Zuleta [41] who went back to an earlier idea employing once again the modified 5-dimensional Vaidya-type metric (5). Allowing the mass to be a function of both the fifth and the time coordinate, this metric provides a reasonable ansatz for a perturbed Schwarzschild background on the brane, ideal for investigating both the localization of the black hole singularity as well as the existence of a static solution. In the previous use of (5) in [8] only ordinary theories of scalar or gauge fields were accounted, which failed to provide a viable solution. In the new approach the authors allowed themselves a greater freedom regarding the nature of the scalar fields considered. The idea was to assume that the black hole mass function has an exponential form capable of canceling the singular term in the value of the invariant curvature quantity $R^{MNP\Sigma}R_{MNP\Sigma}$ appearing in eq. (4) (which is responsible for the infinitely long black string result discussed in the introduction), while reducing to the Schwarzschild picture on the brane. Then taking advantage of the freedom incorporated in the model (warp factor to be y-dependent but otherwise of arbitrary form, no fine-tuning between brane and bulk parameters) we thought that we could find a specific model that would satisfy the 5-dimensional field equations. The viable bulk solution that would emerge could finally be used to determine the brane content thought the junction conditions. First minimally coupled to gravity but otherwise described by a general Lagrangian scalar fields were studied. A detailed analysis was performed in the cases of a single scalar with a non-canonical kinetic term, its Lagrangian being

$$L_{sc} = \sum_{n=1} f_n(\varphi) \, (\partial^M \varphi \partial_M \varphi)^n + V(\varphi),$$

two interacting scalars with Lagrangian

$$L_{sc} = f^{(1)}(\varphi, \chi)\partial^M \varphi \partial_M \varphi + f^{(2)}(\varphi, \chi)\partial^M \chi \partial_M \chi + V(\varphi, \chi),$$

two interacting scalars with general kinetic terms with Lagrangian

$$L_{sc} = \sum_{n=1} f_n^{(1)}(\varphi, \chi)(\partial^M \varphi \partial_M \varphi)^n + \sum_{n=1} f_n^{(2)}(\varphi, \chi)(\partial^M \chi \partial_M \chi)^n + V(\varphi, \chi)$$

and finally two interacting scalar fields with mixed kinetic terms described by

$$L_{sc} = f^{(1)}(\varphi, \chi)\partial^M \varphi \partial_M \varphi + f^{(2)}(\varphi, \chi)\partial^M \chi \partial_M \chi + f^{(3)}(\varphi, \chi)\partial^M \varphi \partial_M \chi + V(\varphi, \chi).$$

Unfortunately, all field configurations failed to satisfy the corresponding 5-dimensional field equations. Furthermore, as the same analysis can be straightforwardly generalized to allow for more general kinetic and mixing terms, the general result was that models with one or two no minimally-coupled-to-gravity scalars simply cannot do the job.

Next the case of non-minimally coupled scalars was studied. The following action was considered

$$S = \int d^4x \, dy \sqrt{-g} \left[\frac{f(\varphi)}{2\kappa_5^2} R - \frac{1}{2}(\nabla\varphi)^2 - V(\varphi) - \Lambda_5 \right]$$

where both the exact form of $f(\varphi)$ and φ are arbitrary to avoid any unreasonable restrictions on the field configurations. After checking the implications of a coupling function being a power law, a polynomial and an exponential function of the field and proving that all these are dead-end choices, a more general analysis was employed for a $f(\varphi)$ of completely arbitrary form. Finally, a no-go argument was formulated stating that a model of a non-minimally coupled scalar field is altogether inconsistent with the desired black hole mass behavior, as described earlier. Two major conclusions were derived from this work. The first was that the localization of the black hole appears to demand the synergetic action from both the brane and the bulk parameters. The second rather interesting outcome was that even in the case where the black hole mass was postulated to be time-independent, the additional fields required to support the model had to be dynamic. A static black hole configuration was not excluded by the calculations, but nevertheless was shown to be quite hard to build. As we feel that the potential of this method is yet to be exhausted, we have already started a new research program to explore a) whether more delicate mass function variations could be the answer and b) the possibility that a reasonable scalar field configuration could support a viable black hole solution that is not strictly Schwarzschild on the brane, but rather Schwarzschild-like.

Furthermore, a specific analytic calculation based on the AdS$_5$/CFT$_4$ duality remains to be done following the steps of the respective numerical results mentioned in the previous section in order to exploit the insights offered by them. In this case the starting point is to consider an exact Schwarzschild metric at a brane located at the infinite boundary of the AdS spacetime. This gravitational background on the brane, rewritten in a more general way, can get expanded along the bulk to give a Randall-Sundrum brane at a finite proper distance whose induced metric is a perturbed Schwarzschild metric and thus describes a black hole. Then by solving the 5-dimensional field equations one would, in principle, completely determine all model parameters. Obviously, doing all that analytically is far from trivial but in the light of the certainty (thanks to the latest numerical calculations) that realistic black hole solutions are "out there" things just might be a bit easier and some optimism is to be allowed.

Conclusion

Up to now, the Warped Extra Dimension Scenario, although one of the most popular ever suggested in theoretical physics, has failed to pass the black-hole test. Finding a regular black hole solution in this framework is a major challenge not only because it has been proven a not-at-all trivial task but also because the existence of such a solution would enhance the possibilities of this scenario to be a realistic description of the actual spacetime geometry. Furthermore, due to the AdS/CFT duality a classical 5-dimensional black hole metric would allow for the determination of the corresponding quantum-corrected 4-dimensional metric, thus providing us with new, deeper insights about the correlations between quantum mechanics and general relativity. Besides, if strong gravity effects emerge indeed in the few TeV energy regime, possessing an explicit black hole solution is the key factor in order to evaluate the related detector signals to find solid evidence about the existence of extra spacelike dimensions, their number and their geometry.

The prize is too significant to be ignored and that is why since the formulation of the RS models until nowadays the scientific community never ceased to try to discover a viable black hole solution. The quest is still active and open for new ideas, methods and techniques. Hopefully, in the next few years solid results would be reached to elucidate the situation and decisively answer the long lasting questions concerning the existence and the exact form of black holes in the context of the Warped Extra Dimension Scenario with all the far reaching implications that would accompany such a discovery.

References

[1]   Arkani-Hamed, N.; Dimopoulos, S.; Dvali, G. *Phys. Lett. B*, 1998, 429, 263; *Phys. Rev. D*, 1999, 59, 086004.

[2]   Randall, L.; Sundrum, R. *Phys. Rev. Lett.*, 1999, 83, 3370; *Phys. Rev. Lett.*, 1999, 83, 4690.

[3]   Duff, M. J.; Liu, J. T. *Phys. Rev. Lett.*, 2000, 85, 2052-2055.

[4]   Chamblin, A.; Hawking, S. W.; Reall, H. S. *Phys. Rev. D*, 2000, 61, 065007.

[5]   Gregory, R.; Laflamme, L. *Phys. Rev. Lett.*, 1993, 70, 2837; *Nucl. Phys. B*, 1994, 428, 399.

[6]   Gregory, R. *Class. Quant. Grav.*, 2000, 17, L125.

[7]   Kanti, P.; Tamvakis, K. *Phys. Rev. D*, 2002, 65, 084010.

[8]   Kanti, P.; Olasagasti, I.; Tamvakis, K. *Phys. Rev. D*, 2003, 68, 124001.

[9]   Creek, S.; Gregory, R.; Kanti, P.; Mistry, B. *Class. Quant. Grav.*, 2006, 23, 6633.

[10] Frolov, V. P.; Snajdr, M.; Stojkovic, D. *Phys. Rev. D*, 2003, 68, 044002.

[11] Galfard, C.; Germani, C.; Ishibashi, A. *Phys. Rev. D*, 2006, 73, 064014.

[12] Flachi, A.; Pujolas, O.; Sasaki, M.; Tanaka, T., *Phys. Rev. D*, 2006, 73, 125017.

[13] Czinner, V. K. *Phys. Rev. D*, 2013, 88, 124029.

[14] Shiromizu, T.; Maeda, K. i.; Sasaki, M. *Phys. Rev. D*, 2000, 62, 024012.

[15] Dadhich, N.; Maartens, R,; Papadopoulos, P.; Rezania, V. *Phys. Lett. B*, 2000, 487, 1.

[16] Casadio, R.; Fabbri, A.; Mazzacurati, L. *Phys. Rev. D*, 2002, 65, 084040.

[17] Casadio, R.; Mazzacurati, L. *Mod. Phys. A*, 2003, 18, 651-660.

[18] Cuadros-Melgar, B.; Papantonopoulos, E.; Tsoukalas, M.; Zamarias, V. *Phys. Rev. Lett.*, 2008, 100, 221601.

[19] Kofinas, G.; Papantonopoulos, E.; Zamarias, V. *Phys. Rev. D*, 2000, 66, 104028.

[20] Karasik, D.; Sahabandu, C.; Suranyi, P.; Wijewardhana, L. C. R. *Phys. Rev. D*, 2004, 70, 064007.

[21] Casadio. R.; Ovalle, J. *Phys. Lett. B*, 2012, 715, 251.

[22] Kudoh, H.; Tanaka, T.; Nakamura, T. *Phys. Rev. D*, 2002, 68, 024035.

[23] Kudoh, H. *Phys. Rev. D*, 2004, 69, 104019; *Phys. Rev. D*, 2004, 70, 029901.

[24] Tanahashi, N.; Tanaka, T. *JHEP*, 2008, 0803, 041.

[25] Yoshino, H. *JHEP*, 2009, 0901, 068.

[26] Tanaka, T. *Prog. Theor. Phys. Suppl.*, 2003, 148, 307.

[27] Bruni, M.; Germani, C.; Maartens, R. *Phys. Rev. Lett.*, 2001, 87, 231302.

[28] Emparan, R.; Fabbri, A.; Kaloper, N. *JHEP*, 2002, 0208, 043.

[29] Fitzpatrick, A. L.; Randall, L.; Wiseman, T. *JHEP*, 2006, 0611, 033.

[30] Gregory, R.; Ross, S. F.; Zegers, R. *JHEP*, 2008, 0809, 029.

[31] Heydari-Fard, M.; Sepangi, H. R. *JCAP*, 2009, 0902, 029.

[32] Dai, D. -C.; Stojkovic, D. *Phys. Lett. B*, 2011, 704, 354.

[33] Bruni, M.; Germani, C.; Maartens, R. *Phys. Rev. Lett.*, 2001, 87, 231302.

[34] Govender, M.; Dadhich, N. *Phys. Lett. B,* 2002, 538, 233.

[35] Kofinas, G.; Papantonopoulos, E. *JCAP*, 2004, 0412, 011.

[36] Tanaka, T. *Prog. Theor. Phys. Suppl.*, 2003, 148, 307.

[37] Emparan, R.; Fabbri, A.; Kaloper, N. *JHEP,* 2002, 0208, 043.

[38] Emparan, R.; Garcia-Bellido, J.; Kaloper, N. *JHEP,* 2003, 0301, 079.

[39] Figueras, P.; Wiseman, T. *Phys. Rev. Lett.,* 2011, 107, 081101.

[40] Abdolrahimi, S.; Cattoen, C.; Page, D. N.; Yaghoobpour-Tari, S. *Phys. Lett. B,* 2013, 720, 405-409; *JCAP*, 2013, 1306, 039.

[41] Kanti, P.; Pappas, N.; Zuleta, K. *Class. Quant. Grav.,* 2013, 30, 235017.

In: Advances in Black Holes Research
Editor: Abraham Barton

ISBN: 978-1-63463-168-6
© 2015 Nova Science Publishers, Inc.

Chapter 4

GRAVITATIONAL COLLAPSE IN ALTERNATIVE THEORIES OF GRAVITY

Jackson Levi Said[*]
Institute of Space Sciences and Astronomy,
University of Malta, Msida, Malta

Abstract

General relativity has been extremely successful in describing gravitation in the solar system regime. However when looking at the galactic, cosmological and infinitesimal scales of the universe the model appears to meet a number of observational and theoretical problems. In order to retain the positive parts of the model while complementing the model with ramifications to better fit the observational evidence, modified theories of gravity have been proposed. These are tested against data as well as against the theoretical issues that arise in general relativity itself.

In the present case the situation of gravitational collapse is investigated. The traditional general relativistic case is review with modifications for the so-called $f(R)$ class of theories. Various examples of particular $f(R)$ functions are explored. Other theories of gravity are then expanded upon with a look into their consequences for gravitational collapse. Finally the eventual fate of a collapsed system is reviewed.

I. Introduction

If beauty were the rubric on which theories of gravity were judged then Einstein's general relativity would be sufficient to curb any currently available alternative. However the scientific burden of proof rests on producing models that have the greatest predictive powers against the quality and amount of hypotheses they provide, essentially Occam's razor. In this light it remains unclear whether Einstein's theory is the best description of gravity that can be achieved given the observations currently available.

General relativity (the standard theory) functions well in terms of predictions on the solar system scale. It is only when the galactic scale is investigated that deviations occur [100, 12]. Peering out beyond the solar system onto the galactic scale a large amount of *dark*

---

[*]E-mail address: jsai0004@um.edu.mt

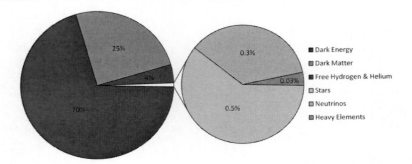

Figure 1. Pie chart depicting of the energy budget of the universe [71].

matter, exceeding 90 % of the total mass in the Milky Way (for example [11]), must be put into the model artificially for the standard theory to reproduce the galactic velocity profile observed. In this limit the terms in general relativity that deviate from Newtonian gravity vanish in that the strong field corrections given by general relativity to Newtonian gravity are negligible, and so this is also a Newtonian gravity result. Thus if it is not the case that this dark matter exists then it must be not only that the general relativistic generalization is incorrect on galactic scales but also that whatever theory is finally admitted must generalize the Newtonian theory scale-wise as well.

Looking at an even larger scale, that of the cosmos itself, again dark matter combined with the standard theory does not explain the observations made. Indeed not only is the universe expanding but accelerating in this expansion [75], and so a second component of the dark universe must be added, namely *dark energy*. Existing in equal density throughout the universe this energy should express itself as a negative pressure that works to expand the very space between material bodies. Together the two components of the dark universe redress the deficiencies of Einstein's theory such that the final model is one that can span the whole breadth of observations currently available. Thus for observation to fit general relativity one must posit the existence of a large quantity of unevidenced mass-energy on the order of $\sim 95\%$ [50] in terms of the energy budget of the universe, shown in Fig.(1). It may be that the vast majority of the universe is indeed dark in all cases except the gravitational one, however until falsifiable evidence can be gathered it is worthwhile to venture into alternative theories of gravity that target these potential deficiencies in general relativity.

Before venturing into the particulars of the alternatives to Einstein's general relativity theory consider first the theory in its action formalism [58]

$$S_{GR} = \frac{1}{16\pi G} \int d^4x \sqrt{-g}\, R + \int d^4x \sqrt{-g}\, \mathcal{L}_M, \tag{1}$$

where $\mathcal{L}_M$ is the lagrangian for the matter fields. By taking a variation of this with respect to the metric tensor and using the least action principle the field equations

$$G_{\mu\nu} \equiv R_{\mu\nu} - \frac{1}{2}g_{\mu\nu}R = 8\pi G T_{\mu\nu}, \tag{2}$$

are derived, where $T_{\mu\nu}$ is the stress-energy tensor and $G_{\mu\nu}$ is the *Einstein tensor* [24]. The first modification to these equations was implanted by Einstein himself where the Lagrangian in Eq.(1) is replaced by $R + \Lambda$. The repercussions of this generalization are that a term is added to the LHS of Eq.(2). This term is $\Lambda g_{\mu\nu}$ and finds its physical significance as the energy density of empty space, i.e., the vacuum energy. This modification was subsequently retracted since it gave rise to accelerating cosmologies which at the time were considered unlikely by most. It was only towards the end of the last century [75] that the model started to be accepted and is now part of the standard cosmological theory. Despite this success a number of outstanding problems persist in gravitation some of which require a fundamental revision in the theory.

Another prominent with general relativity is that of renormalization, general relativity contains an ultraviolet divergence [49]. Given the Lagrangian in Eq.(1) the theory is found to inherently be non-renormalizable meaning that it cannot be contorted into a quantum theory of gravity without modifying some part of its current form. If the theory is to also work on the very small scales of the universe then it will have to be corrected for these scales since in its current form it gives divergences.

The eventual solution to these and other issues in gravitational theory will have, to varying amounts, an effect on the physical processes involves in collapse theory since gravitational collapse offers a process that starts off on the scale of gravity where it is well behaved and conforms well with observation while its end state is one where gravity theory still gives problems. Saying this the different theories do show some deviations from one another. This may be expressed through differences in maximum mass allowances before collapse begins or rates of collapses as well as differences in the eventual state of a collapsing body. In this case study the proper time (i.e., time as measured by an observer on the outer shell of the collapsing body) for collapse is compared for different theories of gravity with a focus on disqualifications achieved for any new coupling parameters.

Stars in general can sustain radial sizes much larger than the Sun however once nuclear fusion reactions begin to dwindle and the nuclear fuel powering the star nears exhaustion the eventual fate of the body becomes much more of an ordered affair with mass being the deciding factor since at this point the rotational parameter will be close to zero as will the charge of the star. As this happens the hydrostatic equilibrium between the inward collapsing matter fields and the outward pushing radiation pressure (resulting from the central fusion furnace) is disturbed, the star starts to shed part of its outer layers. Depending on the eventual mass of the remnant different processes take place. For small remnants the body continues to radiate part of its energy with a lessening of intensity over time, with the whole process lasting longer than the age of the Universe. However for bodies not performing nuclear fusion with masses higher than about $1.44 M_{\odot}$ (1.44 × solar masses) [23] eventual collapse is predicted by general relativity unless other factors such as significant angular momentum or excessive charge are involved. In recent observations there is evidence that this limit may have been exceeded by some stars [46]. Hence it is important to study maximum sizes in not just standard gravity but also in its alternatives.

On a more theoretical note, in general relativity, given a spherically symmetric spacetime the EFEs must give a solution that is static and asymptotically flat, meaning that at infinity the influence of the body is nil. This is known as Birkhoff's theorem [14] with a similar conclusion for the nonvanishing cosmological case [78]. However the cosmological constant case need not be considered here since the effect of a nonzero cosmological constant has little to no effect on the vast majority of timeline in the process of collapse. The main conclusion of the theorem is that any spherically symmetric solution is thus isometric to the Schwarzschild metric below [34]

$$d\tau^2 = \left(1 - \frac{2MG}{r}\right) dt^2 - \left(1 - \frac{2MG}{r}\right)^{-1} dr^2 - r^2 \left(d\theta^2 + \sin^2\theta \, d\phi^2\right). \tag{3}$$

This is not to say that different solutions cannot be useful in studying different aspects of behavior for a spherically symmetric system, but that it can always be transformed into the standard Schwarzschild form. Birkhoff's theorem is not always a feature of an alternative theory of gravity. In fact in cases where it is not satisfied to a sufficient degree certain strange behaviour emerges such as structural dependence of gravitational forces [29]. Thus whether or not the theorem is satisfied is of some import for the theory under consideration.

Unless otherwise stated the signature $(-, +, +, +)$ is to be assumed throughout the following. Also throughout the work Latin indices refer to space-like coordinates only, while Greek indices will refer to general spacetime coordinates. Additionally natural units where $c = 1 = G = \hbar = k_B$ are used unless explicitly stated otherwise.

The review is divided down as follows, the traditional general relativistic spherically symmetric collapse case is first presented which is followed by its direct generalization to the $f(R)$ theory case. Following this gravitational collapse is compared and contrasted over the vast array of alternative theories of gravity. A closing note is then given which discusses the eventual fate of the black hole singularity.

II. Spherically Symmetric Collapse in General Relativity

The spherically symmetric case is considered first since it opens many of the issues that plague a clear understanding of how gravitational collapse leads to a black hole. Here the standard picture of gravitational collapse will be presented [93, 58, 24, 92]

In this symmetry the full ten metric degrees of freedom are first limited to four by taking into account that due to spherical symmetry only the diagonal entries are allowed for the azimuthal angle, ϕ, and the polar angle, θ. The time and radial coordinates may have nonvanishing components for the full combination of possibilities. Secondly, again, to preserve spherical symmetry in every outward direction, the metric components cannot vary over the two angular coordinates. Thus giving the metric ansatz for the proper time, τ, as

$$d\tau^2 = C(r,t) \, dt^2 - D(r,t) \, dr^2 - 2E(r,t) \, drdt - F(r,t)r^2 \left(d\theta^2 + \sin^2\theta \, d\phi^2\right), \tag{4}$$

for the system. By transforming the time coordinate by the arbitrary function $f(\mathbf{x})$, where $\mathbf{x}$ represents a position on the spacetime manifold,

$$t' \rightarrow t + f(\mathbf{x}) \qquad \mathbf{x}' \rightarrow \mathbf{x}. \tag{5}$$

This transformation turns the time-time component of the metric tensor into unity. Thus, suppressing primes, the geodesic equation gives

$$0 = \frac{d^2 x^i}{d\tau^2} = \Gamma^i_{tt} = g^{ij} g_{jt,t}. \tag{6}$$

Since g^{ij} is, in general, nonzero this implies that $g_{jt,t}$ and so the time dependence in $E(r,t)$ falls. Then making the choice of relating $f(\cdot)$ and $E(r,t)$ through the relation [93]

$$f(\cdot) = -2\int^r E(r)\,dr, \tag{7}$$

gives the final metric ansatz as

$$d\tau^2 = dt^2 - U(r,t)\,dr^2 - V(r,t)\left(d\theta^2 + \sin^2\theta\,d\phi^2\right), \tag{8}$$

with a more representational number of degrees of freedom.

For a collapsing compact body the stress-energy tensor of a perfect fluid is used to model the system with [76]

$$T^{\mu\nu} = \rho\,u^\mu u^\nu + p\left(g^{\mu\nu} + u^\mu u^\nu\right), \tag{9}$$

where $\rho(r,t)$ is the energy density and $p(r,t)$ is the pressure. u^μ is the four-velocity of the fluid. For a comoving coordinate system that is freely falling with the fluid space-like velocity profile

$$u^i = 0, \tag{10}$$

and by the four-velocity normalizing condition $g_{\mu\nu}u^\mu u^\nu = -1$, it turns out that $u^t = 1/\sqrt{-g_{tt}} = 1$. Given a freely falling collapsing fluid the pressure contribution will be negligible for simple systems, i.e., $p = 0$. For this system the stress-energy must be conserved since no exchange is present, thus the $T^\mu{}_{\nu;\mu} \equiv 0$, where ; represents the covariant derivative. Taking just the energy conservation part of this implies that

$$0 = T^\mu{}_{t;\mu} = -\frac{\partial\rho}{\partial t} - \rho\Gamma^\nu_{\nu t} = -\frac{\partial\rho}{\partial t} - \rho\left(\frac{\dot{U}}{2U} + \frac{\dot{V}}{V}\right), \tag{11}$$

which can be compressed to one term in the form

$$\frac{\partial}{\partial t}\left(\rho V\sqrt{U}\right) = 0. \tag{12}$$

Given both geometry and stress-energy elements of the collapsing fluid, the governing Einstein field equations (EFEs) can be employed to determine the particular form of the metric components by means of [93]

$$R_{\mu\nu} = -8\pi G S_{\mu\nu}, \tag{13}$$

where

$$S_{\mu\nu} = T_{\mu\nu} - \frac{1}{2}g_{\mu\nu}T, \tag{14}$$

and $R_{\mu\nu}$ is the Ricci tensor. $T = T^\mu{}_\mu$ is the determinant of the stress-energy tensor, and $S_{\mu\nu} = \rho\left(\frac{1}{2}g_{\mu\nu} + u_\mu u_\nu\right)$. These equations are a re-representation of the EFEs in Eq.(2) where a contraction over the two free indices is taken to express the Ricci scalar in terms of stress-energy tensor elements.

Calculating the nonvanishing Ricci tensor components gives

$$R_{tt} = \frac{\ddot{U}}{2U} + \frac{\ddot{V}}{V} - \frac{\dot{U}^2}{4U^2} - \frac{\dot{V}^2}{2V^2}, \tag{15}$$

$$R_{rr} = \frac{V''}{V} - \frac{V'^2}{2V^2} - \frac{U'V'}{2UV} - \frac{\ddot{U}}{2} + \frac{\dot{U}^2}{4U} - \frac{\dot{U}\dot{V}}{2V}, \tag{16}$$

$$R_{\phi\phi} = R_{\theta\theta}\sin^2\theta = \left(-1 + \frac{V''}{2U} - \frac{V'U'}{4U^2} - \frac{\ddot{V}}{2} - \frac{\dot{V}\dot{U}}{4U}\right)\sin^2\theta, \tag{17}$$

$$R_{tr} = \frac{\dot{V}'}{V} - \frac{V'\dot{V}}{2V^2} - \frac{\dot{U}V'}{2UV}. \tag{18}$$

Similarly the $S_{\mu\nu}$ tensor components are determined for nonvanishing components

$$S_{tt} = \frac{\rho}{2}, \qquad S_{rr} = \rho\frac{U}{2}, \qquad S_{\phi\phi} = S_{\theta\theta}\sin^2\theta = \left(\rho\frac{V}{2}\right)\sin^2\theta. \tag{19}$$

Additionally of note is the cross component $S_{tr} = 0$. Combining both geometry and stress-energy components through the EFEs gives

$$\frac{1}{U}\left(\frac{V''}{V} - \frac{V'^2}{2V^2} - \frac{U'V'}{2UV}\right) - \frac{\ddot{U}}{2U} + \frac{\dot{U}^2}{4U^2} - \frac{\dot{U}\dot{V}}{2UV} = -4\pi G\rho, \tag{20}$$

$$-\frac{1}{V} + \frac{1}{U}\left(\frac{V''}{2V} - \frac{U'V'}{4UV}\right) - \frac{\ddot{V}}{2V} - \frac{\dot{V}\dot{U}}{4VU} = -4\pi G\rho, \tag{21}$$

$$\frac{\ddot{U}}{2U} + \frac{\ddot{V}}{V} - \frac{\dot{U}^2}{4U^2} - \frac{\dot{V}^2}{2V^2} = -4\pi G\rho, \tag{22}$$

$$\frac{\dot{V}'}{V} - \frac{V'\dot{V}}{2V^2} - \frac{\dot{U}V'}{2UV} = 0. \tag{23}$$

For this simple model the energy density can be taken as position independent. Also the metric component dependencies can be taken as being separable so that

$$U = A^2(t)f(r), \qquad\qquad V = S^2(t)g(r). \tag{24}$$

Substituting this into Eq.(23), after simplification, gives the relation

$$\frac{\dot{S}}{S} = \frac{\dot{A}}{A}, \tag{25}$$

which implies an equation between S and A up to a constant. Thus f and g can be normalised to give

$$S(t) = A(t). \tag{26}$$

Along a similar line of reasoning the radial coordinate is transformed through $\tilde{r} \to \sqrt{g(r)}$ so that the U and V radial dependencies turn out to be

$$\tilde{f} = \frac{fg'}{4g}, \qquad\qquad \tilde{g} = \tilde{r}^2, \tag{27}$$

which gives metric components

$$U = A^2(t)f(r), \qquad\qquad V = A^2(t)r^2, \qquad (28)$$

where the tildas have been dropped. Here the time dependence is assumed to be the same for both tensor components. However if both dependencies are allowed to vary arbitrarily then on consideration of the isotropic and homogeneous collapse of the fluid, they turn out to be equal by a combination of field equations. Any radial variance is absorbed by $f(r)$.

On applying the separable solution to the EFEs Eqs.(20,21)

$$-\frac{f'(r)}{rf^2(r)} - \ddot{A}(t)A(t) - 2\dot{A}^2(t) = -4\pi G A^2(t)\rho(t), \qquad (29)$$

$$\left(-\frac{1}{r^2} + \frac{1}{rf^2(r)} - \frac{f'(r)}{2rf^2(r)}\right) - \ddot{A}(t)A(t) - 2\dot{A}^2(t) = -4\pi G A^2(t)\rho(t). \qquad (30)$$

Due to all terms in Eqs.(29,30) being equal except for the first ones, it follows that they must be equal and furthermore constant. This constant can be arbitrarily set to $-2k$ where k is some real number such that

$$-\frac{f'(r)}{rf^2(r)} = -\frac{1}{r^2} + \frac{1}{rf^2(r)} - \frac{f'(r)}{2rf^2(r)} \equiv -2k, \qquad (31)$$

which has the simple solution [93]

$$f(r) = \left[1 - kr^2\right]^{-1}. \qquad (32)$$

This leaves only $\rho(t)$ and $A(t)$ left to be determined.

Considering the energy conservation relation in Eq.(12) it follows that $\rho(t)A^3(t)$ is a constant. Taking the normalizing condition

$$A(0) = 1, \qquad (33)$$

the energy density relationship

$$\rho(t) = \rho(0)A^{-3}(t), \qquad (34)$$

is then found. Using Eq.(29) and the as yet unused Eq.(22) gives the simultaneous pair of differential equations governing $A(t)$

$$-2k - \ddot{A}(t)A(t) - 2\dot{A}^2(t) = -4\pi G \rho(0)A^{-1}(t), \qquad (35)$$

$$\ddot{A}(t)A(t) = -\frac{4\pi G}{3}\rho(0)A^{-1}(t). \qquad (36)$$

Adding both the equations eliminates the second time derivative of $A(t)$ which results in

$$\dot{A}^2(t) = -k + \frac{8\pi G}{3}\rho(0)A^{-1}(t). \qquad (37)$$

In order to solve this, a second initial is added to Eq.(33) such that

$$\dot{A}(0) = 0, \qquad (38)$$

which through Eq.(37) implies that

$$k = \frac{8\pi G}{3} \rho(0).$$ (39)

Hence Eq.(37) can be written as

$$\dot{A}^2(t) = k \left(A^{-1}(t) - 1 \right).$$ (40)

This is solved by the set of parametric equations for a cycloid

$$t = \frac{\psi + \sin\psi}{2\sqrt{k}},$$ (41)

$$A(t) = \frac{1}{2} \left(1 + \cos\psi \right).$$ (42)

From the preceding relation the time taken for the fluid to completely collapse, $t(\psi_0) = T$ can be found by determining at which point R vanishes. Thus the working definition of total collapse will be taken as the total time taken for the classical calculation of the radius to reduce to zero. For the time equation this occurs when $\psi = \pi$, which means that

$$T = \frac{\pi}{2\sqrt{k}} = \frac{\pi}{2} \left(\frac{3}{8\pi G\rho(0)} \right)^{1/2}.$$ (43)

Leaving $A(t)$ in this form the solution for the metric tensor turns out to be

$$d\tau^2 = dt^2 - A^2(t) \left[\frac{dr^2}{1 - kr^2} + r^2 \left(d\theta^2 + \sin^2\theta \, d\phi^2 \right) \right].$$ (44)

From the above analysis it may be concluded that a fluid of initial uniform density $\rho(0)$ with zero pressure will collapse from rest to a state of infinite proper energy density in a finite time T. This applies only to the physical system in the comoving coordinates. For an observer at infinity a different series of events is seen during the final phases of collapse.

As noted in the introduction, for an observer at infinity there always exists a coordinate system in which the geometry of a spherically symmetric body can be described by Eq.(3). By matching the interior and exterior solutions in Eq.(44) and Eq.(3), the constant k in the interior metric can be used to relate the interior solution with the Birkhoff parameters, i.e., system mass [14].

To achieve this the interior metric will have to be transformed from the Gaussian normal form it is in, where the proper time and observer time are equal, to the Birkhoff form where the negative of the time-time component and the inverse of the radial-radial components are equal. Considering first the spatial coordinates, it is straightforward to see that (r, θ, ϕ) must be changed to

$$\bar{r} \to rA(t), \qquad\qquad \bar{\theta} \to \theta, \qquad\qquad \bar{\phi} \to \phi,$$ (45)

coordinates. The problem now is how to choose a transformation of the time-like coordinate such that the cross term of the preceding transformation are eliminated. First the space-like coordinate transformations are implemented with the help of Eq.(40) which gives

$$d\tau^2 = \left(\frac{A^2 \left[1 - k\frac{\bar{r}^2}{A^2} \right] - \bar{r}^2 k \frac{1-A}{A}}{A^2 \left(1 - k\frac{\bar{r}^2}{A^2} \right)} \right) dt^2 - \frac{2\bar{r}\sqrt{k\left(\frac{1-A}{A}\right)}\, d\bar{r}\, dt}{A\left(k\frac{\bar{r}^2}{A^2} - 1 \right)} - \frac{d\bar{r}^2}{1 - k\frac{\bar{r}^2}{A^2}} - \bar{r}^2 d\bar{\theta}^2 - \bar{r}^2 \sin^2\bar{\theta}\, d\bar{\phi}^2,$$ (46)

a transformation of the time-like coordinate is required of the form

$$d\bar{t} = \eta(r,t) \left[\left(\frac{A^2 \left[1 - k\frac{\bar{r}^2}{A^2}\right] - \bar{r}^2 k\frac{1-A}{A}}{A^2 \left(1 - k\frac{\bar{r}^2}{A^2}\right)} \right) dt - \frac{\bar{r}\sqrt{k\left(\frac{1-A}{A}\right)}d\bar{r}}{A\left(k\frac{\bar{r}^2}{A^2} - 1\right)} \right], \tag{47}$$

such that $\eta(r,t)$ is chosen so that the resulting metric is an exact differential, and so

$$\frac{\partial}{\partial r}\left[\eta(r,t)\left(\frac{A^2\left[1 - k\frac{\bar{r}^2}{A^2}\right] - \bar{r}^2 k\frac{1-A}{A}}{A^2\left(1 - k\frac{\bar{r}^2}{A^2}\right)}\right)\right] = -\frac{\partial}{\partial t}\left[\eta(r,t)\frac{\bar{r}\sqrt{k\left(\frac{1-A}{A}\right)}d\bar{r}}{A\left(k\frac{\bar{r}^2}{A^2} - 1\right)}\right]. \tag{48}$$

This results in the new time coordinate being described by [93]

$$\bar{t} = \left(\frac{1 - ka^2}{k}\right)^{1/2} \int_{S(r,t)}^{1} \frac{dA}{1 - \frac{ka^2}{A}} \left(\frac{A}{1-A}\right)^{1/2}, \tag{49}$$

where the function $S(r,t)$ is given by

$$S(r,t) = 1 - \left(\frac{1 - kr^2}{1 - ka^2}\right)^{1/2}(1 - A). \tag{50}$$

The constant a is an arbitrary constant and may be set to the radius of the fluid in the comoving coordinates. Therefore taking a 'standard' form metric

$$d\tau^2 = B(\bar{r},\bar{t})d\bar{t}^2 - \tilde{A}(\bar{r},\bar{t})d\bar{r}^2 - \bar{r}^2\left(d\bar{\theta}^2 + \sin^2\bar{\theta}d\bar{\phi}^2\right), \tag{51}$$

the components turn out to be

$$B(r,t) = \frac{A}{S}\left(\frac{1 - kr^2}{1 - ka^2}\right)^{1/2}\frac{(1 - ka^2/S)^2}{1 - kr^2/A}, \tag{52}$$

$$\tilde{A}(r,t) = \left(1 - \frac{kr^2}{A}\right)^{-1}. \tag{53}$$

While the preceding relations are quite cumbersome, on the fluid radius ($r = a$) they simplify to the required Birkhoff form

$$\bar{t} = \left(\frac{1 - ka^2}{k}\right)^{1/2} \int_{A(t)}^{1} \frac{dA}{1 - \frac{ka^2}{A}} \left(\frac{A}{1-A}\right)^{1/2}, \tag{54}$$

$$B(\bar{a},\bar{t}) = 1 - \frac{ka^2}{A(t)}, \tag{55}$$

$$\tilde{A}(\bar{a},\bar{t}) = \left(1 - \frac{ka^2}{A(t)}\right)^{-1}. \tag{56}$$

On matching with the interior solution the metric components are continuous at $\bar{r} = aA(t)$ if

$$k = \frac{2MG}{a^3}. \tag{57}$$

Using Eq.(39) gives the expected mass-density formula for a spherical body

$$M = \frac{4\pi}{3}\rho(0)a^3. \tag{58}$$

Now that the entire spacetime surrounding the collapsing fluid has been described, the discussion can return to the initial problem of what does an observer at infinity measure as the fluid collapses through its Schwarzschild radius at $2GM$. Consider a light signal emitted radially outwards from radius $\bar{r}$ and at time $\bar{t}$ during collapse. For an observer at $\bar{r}'$ the arrival time of the signal will be given by

$$\bar{t}' = \bar{t} + \int_{aA(t)}^{\bar{r}'} \left(1 - \frac{2MG}{\bar{r}}\right)^{-1} d\bar{r}. \tag{59}$$

the conclusion of this relationship is that as

$$\bar{r} \to 2GM, \tag{60}$$

or $A(t) \to \frac{2GM}{a} = ka^2$, that for an observer at infinity the collapse begins to take exceedingly longer to proceed such that the collapse begins to crawl as it approaches the Schwarzschild radius, and that total collapse beyond this radius is impossible to observe in terms of the radius of the fluid.

In parallel with the collapsing of the fluid body, any outgoing signals begin to suffer a growing gravitational redshift. Thus as the collapse appears to slow down, it simultaneously begins to fade out of sight. As the spherical radius, $\bar{r}$, decreases the proper time interval between wave crests being emitted is equal to the comoving time, t. Since natural units are chosen then the time interview between crests will be exactly equal to the emitted wavelength, λ_0. The time interval $d\bar{t}'$ in the 'standard' coordinate system, at $\bar{r}'$, is then given by λ'. Therefore the fractional change in wavelength will be given by [93]

$$z \equiv \frac{\lambda' - \lambda_0}{\lambda_0} = \frac{d\bar{t}'}{dt} - 1 = \frac{d\bar{t}}{dt} - a\dot{A}(t)\left(1 - \frac{2MG}{aA(t)}\right)^{-1} - 1 \tag{61}$$

$$= -\dot{A}(t)\left(1 - \frac{ka^2}{A(t)}\right)^{-1}\left[\left(\frac{1 - ka^2}{k}\right)^{1/2}\left(\frac{A(t)}{1 - A(t)}\right)^{1/2} + a\right] - 1. \tag{62}$$

Using Eq.(37) simplifies this to

$$z = \left(1 - \frac{ka^2}{A(t)}\right)^{-1}\left[(1 - ka^2)^{1/2} + a\sqrt{k}\left(\frac{1 - A(t)}{A(t)}\right)^{1/2}\right] - 1. \tag{63}$$

For most astrophysical interesting sources, consider a stellar sphere that is initially much larger than its Schwarzschild radius, i.e.

$$ka^2 = \frac{2GM}{a} \ll 1, \tag{64}$$

where two distinct periods can be distinguished by means of the point at which the Schwarzschild radius is crossed. Taking these cases in turn.

As Collapse Begins

During this phase of collapse it is also true that

$$\frac{ka^2}{A(t)} \ll 1. \tag{65}$$

This means that $\bar{t}$, $\bar{t}'$ and z can be expressed in the form [93]

$$\bar{t} \simeq t, \tag{66}$$

$$\bar{t}' \simeq \bar{t} + \bar{r}' - aA(t) \simeq t + \bar{r}' - aA(t) \simeq t + \bar{r}', \tag{67}$$

$$z \simeq a\sqrt{k} \left(\frac{1 - A(t)}{A(t)}\right)^{1/2} \simeq a\sqrt{k} \left(\frac{1 - A(\bar{t}' - \bar{r}')}{A(\bar{t}' - \bar{r}')}\right)^{1/2} \tag{68}$$

Collapse to the Schwarzschild Radius

As $\frac{ka^2}{R(t)} \to 1$, the time coordinate in Eq.(44) tends to

$$t \simeq \frac{1}{2\sqrt{k}} \left(\pi - \frac{4}{3} \left(ka^2\right)^{3/2}\right), \tag{69}$$

by Eq.(42). This means that [93]

$$\bar{t} \simeq -ka^3 \ln\left(1 - \frac{ka^2}{A(t)}\right) + \text{const}, \tag{70}$$

$$\bar{t}' \simeq \bar{t} - ka^3 \ln\left(1 - \frac{ka^2}{A(t)}\right) + \text{const} \simeq -2ka^3 \ln\left(1 - \frac{ka^2}{A(t)}\right) + \text{const}, \tag{71}$$

$$z \simeq 2\left(1 - \frac{ka^2}{A(t)}\right)^{-1} \propto \exp\left(\frac{\bar{t}'}{2ka^3}\right). \tag{72}$$

Combing the results in both phases of the collapse process, it emerges that the redshift of signals being observed at infinity gradually increases from zero while keeping to an order of magnitude of $a\sqrt{k} \ll 1$. This continues until the time nears the proper collapse period $T = \pi/2\sqrt{k}$, at which time the redshift increases exponentially with a rate of $\left(2ka^3\right)^{-1}$. Thus for a collapsing star this means that the star will initially not be redshifted by much until, close to the time the collapsing surface reaches its Schwarzschild radius, the stars suddenly disappears and so becomes a so-called black hole.

Once the star reaches the exponential phase of collapse, by Birkhoff's theorem all that can be extracted about the resulting body is the mass (and the charge and rotation parameter for cases where these are nonzero) [13]. However quantum processes may result in near field perturbations about this picture, within general relativity it remains unclear exactly how such perturbations may interact with the classical collapse seen by an observer at infinity [41, 40, 42].

At this point it is important to recall that the collapse model presented arises for a spherically symmetric body of nonvanishing mass. While the full general rotating solution has not been obtained analytically [28], a number of interesting simulation studies have been done [87, 2, 72]. In the case of spherically symmetric collapse it is only the pressure produced by means of nuclear fusion that holts the collapse, however when the collapse allows for a nonvanishing rotation parameter an element of mass lose is introduced. The issue then arises of where the rotation is significant enough to bring the mass down to a point lower than the limit required to produce a black hole in the first place. That is, if the rotational parameter is too large then enough mass may be lost for the remaining fluid collapse to stabilise with respect to the outward pressure and thus retard the collapse to a single point. It has been shown that for stellar masses just above the *Chandrasekhar limit* (the maximum mass for a stable white dwarf) a rotation parameter of less than half the maximum ($a \simeq 0.5$) is allowable but anything over will tear apart [82] significant parts of the outer layer. However the full analytic problem appear too complex to be solved using the current toolbox of mathematical techniques.

III.   Collapse in f(R) Gravity

The most popular and widely studied modification of general relativity is encompassed in the so-called $f(R)$ gravity models. In this approach the Ricci scalar in the cation for standard gravity, Eq.(1) is generalized to an arbitrary function $f(R)$ such that the gravity action is then given by [27]

$$S_{GR} = \frac{1}{16\pi G} \int d^4x \sqrt{-g}\, f(R) + \int d^4x \sqrt{-g}\, \mathcal{L}_M. \tag{73}$$

$f(R)$ gravity comes in three generic flavours in that there are three techniques to dealing with the mathematics of the generalization approach. these represent different approaches to the underlying physical processes of the gravitational field proposed. The simplest modification is the metric formalism which takes wholesale the exact approach of general relativity. The difference between the two theories is bourn out through the modifications to the field equations and not through any underlying alterations. The other two formalisms of $f(R)$ gravity emerge by considering a second connection as being independent of the metric tensor. Thus allowing for a second field on which gravity can propagate. The study of gravitational collapse has been studied in the metric formalism however still lacks a full exploration in the other two expressions of the theory. For a fuller review of the theory [36, 84].

By varying this action with respect to the metric tensor $g^{\mu\nu}$, the modified field equations turn out to be

$$(1 + f_R)R_{\mu\nu} - \frac{1}{2}(R + f(r))g_{\mu\nu} + (\nabla_\mu\nabla_\nu - g_{\mu\nu}\Box)f_R = -8\pi GT_{\mu\nu}, \tag{74}$$

where $f_R \equiv \frac{df(R)}{dR}$ and $\Box \equiv \nabla_\lambda\nabla^\lambda$ is the D'Alembertian operator. With a little manipulation this can be put into a form very similar to the EFEs where the LHS is composed of the same terms as the EFEs and the modified terms along with the stress-energy terms are on the RHS giving

$$R_{\mu\nu} - \frac{1}{2}Rg_{\mu\nu} = \frac{1}{1 + f_R}\left[-8\pi GT_{\mu\nu} - (\nabla_\mu\nabla_\nu - g_{\mu\nu}\Box)f_R + \frac{1}{2}(f(R) - Rf_R)g_{\mu\nu}\right]. \tag{75}$$

This was done to simplify some of the resulting field equations for the system under consideration. Similarly the Ricci scalar can be determined by considering the contraction of Eq.(74) over the free index pair which results in

$$(1 - f_R) R + 2f(R) + 3\Box f_R = 8\pi GT. \tag{76}$$

For an isotropic and homogeneous spacetime the D'Alembertian operator turns out to only have nonvanishing time components and so the solution of Eq.(76) for the Ricci scalar gives

$$R = \frac{8\pi GT - 2f(R) - 3\ddot{f}_R}{1 - f_R}. \tag{77}$$

Again the metric in Eq.(8) is taken as the ansatz, where the system is constrained to being spherically symmetric. Metrics of this kind, where the coordinate time measures the proper time are called *Gaussian normal* metrics [58]. The same stress-energy tensor as in Eq.(9) with vanishing pressure is assumed, and for the same reason the same transformation found in Eq.(28) is taken. By considering the $tt-$, $rr-$ and $\theta\theta-$ modified field equation components, the following relations are found [20]

$$3\frac{\ddot{A}}{A} = \frac{1}{1 + f_R}\left[-8\pi G\rho + 3\frac{\dot{A}}{A}\dot{f}_R + \frac{R + f(R)}{2}\right], \tag{78}$$

$$A\ddot{A} + 2\dot{A}^2 + \frac{f'}{rf^2} = \frac{A^2}{1 + f_R}\left[\ddot{f}_R + 2\frac{\dot{A}}{A}\dot{f}_R + \frac{R + f(R)}{2}\right], \tag{79}$$

$$A\ddot{A} + 2\dot{A}^2 + \frac{1}{r^2} - \frac{1}{fr^2} + \frac{f'}{2rf^2} = \frac{A^2}{1 + f_R}\left[\ddot{f}_R + 2\frac{\dot{A}}{A}\dot{f}_R + \frac{R + f_R}{2}\right]. \tag{80}$$

Browsing over the terms in Eqs.(80,79) it is noted that the RHS of both equations are exactly equal and that terms in A on the LHS are also equal. Furthermore the RHS of both equations depends only on the time coordinate in terms of derivatives. The terms not in A on the LHS all depend on the radial coordinate. Thus these two components must be equal and constant, hence giving

$$\frac{1}{r}\frac{f'}{f^2} = \frac{1}{r^2} - \frac{1}{fr^2} + \frac{1}{2r}\frac{f'}{f^2} \equiv 2k, \tag{81}$$

where k is an arbitrary constant as is taken in the general relativistic case in Eq.(31). Solving this relation gives

$$h(r) = \left(1 - kr^2\right)^{-1}, \tag{82}$$

which is exactly the same as the general relativistic equivalent solution found in Eq.(32). Substituting the solution for f into the radial-radial field equation gives

$$-\frac{\ddot{A}}{A} - 2\left(\frac{\dot{A}}{A}\right)^2 - \frac{2k}{A^2} = \frac{1}{1 + f_R}\left[-\ddot{f}_R - 2\frac{\dot{A}}{A}\dot{f}_R - \frac{R + f(R)}{2}\right]. \tag{83}$$

As in the general relativity case, the energy conservation relation in Eq.(11) leads to the relation Eq.(34) between the density of the fluid and the unknown metric function $A(t)$.

Substituting this relation into Eq.(78) leads to [20]

$$\dot{A}^2 = -k + \frac{1}{1+f_R} \left[\frac{4}{3}\pi G\rho(0)A^{-1} + \frac{A^2\ddot{f}_R}{2} + \frac{A\dot{A}\dot{f}_R}{2} + \frac{A^2}{6}(R + f(R)) \right], \qquad (84)$$

where the solution for $f(r)$ was used. For a fluid that is at rest when $t = 0$, initial conditions of $\dot{A}(t = 0) = 0$ and $A(t = 0) = 1$ hold. Since k is a constant in the preceding equation then it can be evaluated at any point, in particular taking the time to be zero gives

$$k = \frac{1}{1+f_R(R_0)} \left[\frac{4\pi G}{3}\rho_0 + \frac{\ddot{f}_R(R_0)}{2} + \frac{R_0 + f(R_0)}{6} \right], \qquad (85)$$

where $\rho_0 = \rho(t = 0)$ and $R_0 = R(t = 0)$. In this way Eq.(84) can again be used with k and the Ricci scalar substituted for from Eqs.(85,77)

$$\dot{A}^2 = -\frac{1}{6(1-f_R^2(R_0))} \left[8\pi G\rho_0(2 - f_R(R_0)) - f(R_0)(1 + f_R(R_0)) - 3\ddot{f}_R(R_0)f_R(R_0) \right] \qquad (86)$$

$$+ \frac{1}{1-f_R^2} \frac{8\pi G}{3}\rho_0 A^{-1} - \frac{1}{6(1-f_R^2)} \left[8\pi G\rho_0 A^{-1}f_R + 3A^2\ddot{f}_R f_R - 3A\dot{A}\dot{f}_R(1 - f_R) + A^2 f(R)(1 + f_R) \right]. \qquad (87)$$

For particular models of $f(R)$ theories, the preceding equation can be solved perturbatively. $f(R)$ theories will modify A around the general relativistic solution A_{GR} such that

$$A \simeq A_{GR} + g(\psi), \qquad (88)$$

where ψ is the parameter in the parametric solution of Eq.(87). For comparison the GR solution is in Eq.(42). Similarly the arbitrary function, $f(R)$, itself can be expanded about the GR Ricci scalar value

$$f(R) \simeq f(R_{GR}) + f_R(R_{GR})(R - R_{GR}). \qquad (89)$$

The effect of the particular form of the modified action in the Lagrangian may be anything from first order onwards, meaning that the function $g(\psi)$ in Eq.(88) may even have a first order effect. Thus substituting both these expansions, Eqs.(88,89), into Eq.(87) and keeping only terms up to first order gives

$$\tan\left(\frac{\psi}{2}\right)g' = -\frac{1}{2}\cos^{-2}\left(\frac{\psi}{2}\right)g + \frac{1}{12k}\cos^2\left(\frac{\psi}{2}\right)(f(R_{GR_0}) + 3kf_R(R_{GR_0})) - \frac{1}{4}f_R(R_{GR}) \qquad (90)$$

$$+ \frac{1}{4\sqrt{k}}\sin\left(\frac{\psi}{2}\right)\cos^3\left(\frac{\psi}{2}\right)\dot{f}_R(R_{GR}) - \frac{1}{12k}\cos^6\left(\frac{\psi}{2}\right)f(R_{GR}), \qquad (91)$$

where the general relativity terms have cancelled out, as expected. This equation can be used to determine $g(\psi)$ up to first order for different models of $f(R)$.
Different $f(R)$ models can now be investigated

Model 1. $f(R) = \epsilon R^2$ This model has been shown to give a viable inflationary cosmology model [85] as well as a potential source of dark matter [21]. In this model the proportionality constant takes the form of

$$\epsilon = \frac{1}{6m_0^2}. \qquad (92)$$

One consequence of the added term in the action for this $f(R)$ model is a fifth force which is mediated by a new scalar graviton particle. By means of torsion-balance experiments a constraint of $m_0 \geq 2.7 \times 10^{-12}$ GeV (at 95% C.L.) is obtained, implying that $\epsilon \leq 2.3 \times 10^{22}$ GeV^{-2}. To avoid Tachyon solutions ϵ must not be allowed to be negative. These constraints are confirmed in Ref.[10].

Substituting the new term into Eq.(91) gives the governing relation

$$g'(\psi) + g(\psi)\mathrm{cosec}(\psi) + \frac{9}{8}k\epsilon\left(\sin\psi + 2\tan\frac{\psi}{2} - 4\tan^4\left(\frac{\psi}{2}\right)\mathrm{cosec}(\psi)\right) = 0. \quad (93)$$

The homogeneous solution of this equation is $g_{\mathrm{Hom}} \propto \cot\left(\frac{\psi}{2}\right)$ which is divergent at $\psi = 0$. The complete analytic solution is given by

$$g(\psi) = c_1 \cot\left(\frac{\psi}{2}\right) - \frac{9}{128}k\epsilon\cot\left(\frac{\psi}{2}\right)\left\{-16\left(\psi + \sin\psi\right) + \frac{64}{5}\tan\left(\frac{\psi}{2}\right)\left[4 - \sec^2\left(\frac{\psi}{2}\right)\left(\sec^2\left(\frac{\psi}{2}\right) - 2\right)\right]\right\}. \quad (94)$$

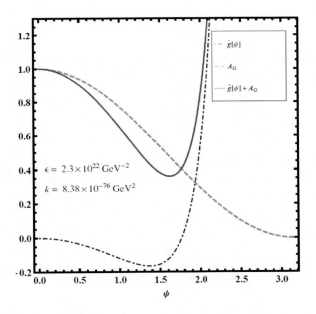

Figure 2. Comparison between the $f(R) = \epsilon R^2$ model ($c_1 = 0$) and the GR result. k is set by Eq.(39) which when computed at the beginning of structure formation (SF), when $z \simeq 1100$, has a value of $\rho_{SF} \simeq 1.5 \times 10^{-38}$ GeV$^4 \simeq 3.5 \times 10^{-18}$ kg/m^3. The initial modification to the process is exceedingly small so much so that $\hat{g}(\psi) = 10^{52}g(\psi)$ is considered instead of $g(\psi)$ so that the variance would be visible [21].

Since $\psi = 0$ is divergent it is not considered in the following analysis. In Figure 2, the collapse process is shown. Initially this is nonexistent such that it grows negatively, thus providing a greater collapse rate. As ψ approaches full collapse at π [20],

$$g(\psi) \simeq \frac{72k\epsilon}{5(\psi - \pi)^4}, \quad (95)$$

which means that total collapse is entirely avoided. At this point the linear perturbation approach for A no longer applies and a more complex analysis must be attempted.

Similarly in the limit as $\psi \to \pi$, the time parametric solution in Eq.(42) approximates to

$$t = \frac{\psi + \sin\psi}{2\sqrt{k}} \simeq \frac{\pi + \frac{1}{6}(\Delta\psi)^3}{2\sqrt{k}}, \tag{96}$$

or when compared with the general relativity result

$$\frac{\Delta t}{t_{GR}} \simeq \frac{(\Delta\psi)^3}{6\pi}. \tag{97}$$

In order to find the parameter space for interesting regions in ϵ, the other part of the parametric solution in Eq.(42) is considered

$$A(t) = \frac{1}{2}(1 + \cos\psi) \simeq \frac{(\psi - \pi)^2}{4}. \tag{98}$$

Interesting effects for collapse would, at the very least, happen when $|g(\psi)| = |A(t)|$ which would certainly occur in the limit as $\psi \to \pi$. Combining both functions in the limit gives the critical value of

$$\psi = \pi - \left(\frac{288|k\epsilon|}{5}\right)^{1/6}. \tag{99}$$

An important point to make at this junction is that the k value in the preceding equation is taken to be the same as its value in the GR case. In principle this should also include other terms depending on $f(R)$ as represented in Eq.(85) however since a comparative result is being determined then only the dominant general relativity term need be taken.

For the more physically interesting situations of collapsing bodies, Eq.(99) with Eq.(85) gives a value of ψ very close to π thus justifying the approach taken. In Figure 3 the density is plotted against the coupling parameter ϵ. As is observed there is a wide range of possible values for ϵ.

Model 2. $f(R) = \epsilon R^{-1}$

Another interesting and possibly cosmologically significant model of the $f(R)$ class of theories is the addition of an inverse term in the Einstein-Hilbert Lagrangian. This has been shown to produce late-time accelerated expansion as well as a number of other significant phenomenological effects [19]. The model is no longer considered physically viable however it is interesting to see how this toy model behaves as compared with general relativity.

Using this model again a governing relation is found for $g(\psi)$ using Eq.(91) which results in

$$g'(\psi) + g(\psi)\operatorname{cosec}\psi = \frac{\epsilon}{6k^2}\sin\left(\frac{\psi}{2}\right)\cos^{13}\left(\frac{\psi}{2}\right). \tag{100}$$

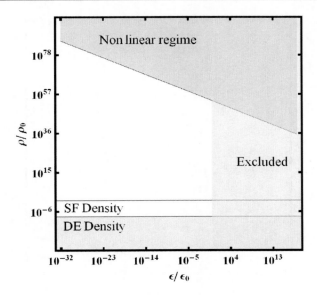

Figure 3. Region of validity of the perturbation regime. The blue region shows at what values the linear approach breaks down, while in yellow the region where $\epsilon > \epsilon_0 = 2.3 \times 10^{-12}\,\mathrm{GeV}^{-2}$ is shown which is excluded by observation. The rest of the parameter space is possible. For reference the density for structure formation and dark energy (DE) are also shown [21].

The full solution turns out to be

$$g(\psi) = c_1 \cot\left(\frac{\psi}{2}\right) + \frac{\epsilon}{6k^2}\left[\frac{33\psi}{2048} + \frac{165\sin\psi}{8192} - \frac{11\sin(2\psi)}{8192} - \frac{121\sin(3\psi)}{24576} - \frac{25\sin(4\psi)}{8192}\right.$$
$$\left. - \frac{43\sin(5\psi)}{40960} - \frac{5\sin(6\psi)}{24576} - \frac{\sin(7\psi)}{57344}\right]\cot\left(\frac{\psi}{2}\right). \tag{101}$$

Similar to the first model the homogeneous solution is ignored since it diverges at $\psi = 0$. Expanding $g(\psi)$ about $\psi = \pi$ gives

$$g(\psi) \simeq -\frac{11\pi\epsilon\,(\psi - \pi)}{8192k^2}, \tag{102}$$

which differs from the previous model in that the ψ bracket now appears in the numerator. This will have consequences for the non-linear regime in the parameter space graph. As in the preceding case the interesting divergences from general relativity happen after the point that $|g(\psi)| = |A(t)|$, meaning after the point

$$\psi \simeq \pi - \frac{11\pi}{2048}\frac{|\epsilon|}{k^2}. \tag{103}$$

In Figure 4 the variance of the modified parameters are compared with the equivalent general relativistic comparisons. As was suggested in Ref.[19], ϵ is set to $-\mu^4$ with $\mu = 10^{-42}\,\mathrm{GeV}$. In this instance the ψ parameter at collapse, ψ_C, does not vary between the

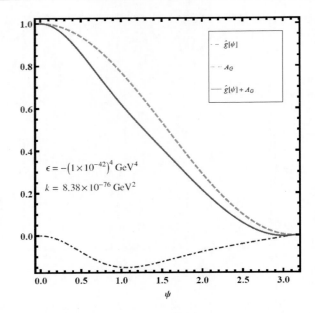

Figure 4. Analogous graph to Figure 2, with $\hat{g}(\psi) = 10^{19}g(\psi)$ [21].

general relativity and $f(R)$ cases. This is also true for cases where $0 > \epsilon > -\mu^4$ however when $\epsilon < \mu^4$ this does not hold anymore. In Figure 5 the regions described are shown. For this model the nonlinear region descreases for growing densities whereas the excluded region is, in this case, a lower bound on the ϵ coupling factor. On the other hand it can also be said that the nonlinear region increases for increasing ϵ values or for lower densities. This last observation turns out to be a general property of $f(R)$ theories which provide late-time accelerated cosmologies, given densities higher than the dark energy. To better understand the results represented in Figure 4 the time ratio similar to Eq.(97) is then considered which gives [20]

$$\frac{\Delta t}{t_{GR}} \simeq -\frac{11^3 \epsilon^3 \pi^2}{3k^6 2^{34}}.$$ (104)

This correction becomes less significant as the density of the object grows. This observation fits in with the fact that the correction in $g(\psi)$ to the general relativity result is proportional to ϵ/k^2, whereas $k \propto \rho_0$. Thus higher density objects will suffer a smaller modification and so a shorter time variance as compared with general relativity.

Model 3. $f(R) = \lambda R_0 \left[\left(1 + \frac{R^2}{R_0}\right)^{-n} - 1\right]$

Finally the Starobinsky model [86] is investigated. This model has been studied in detail and has shown some interesting results. For compact objects such as neutron stars the Starobinsky model has a couple of fine-tuning problems that may be incompatible with some aspects of inflation [88] however this may not necessarily be such a problem [38] given the latest planck data. For the same data, it has been shown that the model can also be fit into the inflation picture [5] with a scalar field giving rise to the inflationary period.

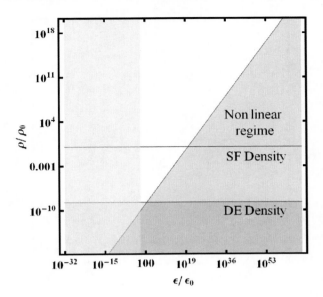

Figure 5. Analogous graph to Figure 3, with $\epsilon_0 = -\mu^4$ and $\mu = 10^{-42}\,\text{GeV}$ [21].

For this model $n, \lambda > 0$ and R_0 is taken to be of the order of magnitude of the cosmological constant. Given this choice of the model parameter R_0 the Starobinsky model becomes a viable theory of gravity. According to Ref.[86] λ can be related to R_0 and the Hubble parameter through

$$H_0^2 = \frac{\lambda R_0}{6}. \tag{105}$$

The value of λ varies depending on the value of the integer n. However a good pair of values that is indicative of how the model works is

$$\lambda = 0.69, \qquad\qquad n = 1, \tag{106}$$

which also keeps the model relatively easy to work with. For this choice of n, the constraint on the modification $g(\psi)$ is governed by

$$-g'(\psi) - g(\psi)\text{cosec}(\psi) - \frac{9k\lambda R_0 \sin^3(\psi)\text{cosec}^4\left(\frac{\psi}{2}\right)}{32\left(9k^2 + R_0^2\right)^2}\left(R_0^2 + 3k^2\right)$$

$$+ \frac{72k\lambda R_0 \sin^4\left(\frac{\psi}{2}\right)\text{cosec}(\psi)}{\left(R_0^2 + 9k^2\sec^{12}\left(\frac{\psi}{2}\right)\right)^2}\left(R_0^2 + 3k^2\sec^{12}\left(\frac{\psi}{2}\right)\right)$$

$$- \frac{9k\lambda R_0^3 \tan\left(\frac{\psi}{2}\right)\sec^4\left(\frac{\psi}{2}\right)\left(R_0^2 - 27k^2\sec^{12}\left(\frac{\psi}{2}\right)\right)}{2\left(9k^2\sec^{12}\left(\frac{\psi}{2}\right) + R_0^2\right)^3} = 0. \tag{107}$$

Dissimilar to the preceding two toy models this $f(R)$ theory equation has no analytic solution as of yet and so numerical solutions must be found for particular values k, λ and R_0.

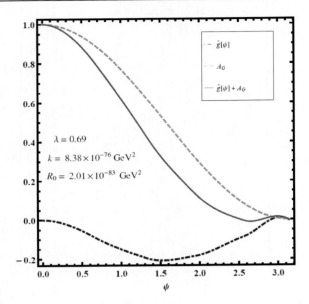

Figure 6. Similar to Figs.(2,4), the modification is shown as a function of the parameter ψ. In this case $\hat{g}(\psi) = 10^9 g(\psi)$ has to be taken to make the modification present observable [21].

In Figure 6 the modification to Eq.(88) is shown for this model of $f(R)$ gravity with realistic parameter values. However without assuming any values of these parameters the limits $\psi \to 0$ and $\psi \to \pi$ can also be studied. As $\psi \to 0$ the governing equation reduces to

$$-g'(\psi) - \frac{g(\psi)}{\psi} - \frac{9k\lambda R_0 \left(3k^2 - R_0^2\right)\psi}{4\left(9k^2 + R_0^2\right)^2} = 0, \qquad (108)$$

which has an analytic solution

$$g(\psi) = \frac{c_1}{\psi} + \frac{3k\lambda R_0 \left(R_0^2 - 3k^2\right)\psi^2}{4\left(9k^2 + R_0^2\right)^2}, \qquad (109)$$

where c_1 is an integration constant. For the solution to be finite in the region of interest $c_1 = 0$ must be set.

On the other end of the collapse spectrum, as $\psi \to \pi$

$$-g'(\psi) + \frac{g(\psi)}{\psi - \pi} + \frac{9k\lambda R_0 \left(\psi - \pi\right)^3 \left(3k^2 + R_0^2\right)}{32\left(9k^2 + R_0^2\right)^2} = 0, \qquad (110)$$

which gives the analytic solution

$$g(\psi) = c_1 \left(\psi - \pi\right) + \frac{3k\lambda R_0 \left(\psi - \pi\right)^4 \left(3k^2 + 2R_0^2\right)}{32\left(9k^2 + R_0^2\right)^2}. \qquad (111)$$

Since this involves higher powers than the general relativity equivalent in Eq.(98), the validity of the linear regime cannot be estimated in this limit. In any case the modification has its most significant effect in the intermediate regime where the collapsing fluid has not yet entered its Schwarzschild radius, as can be observed from Figure 6.

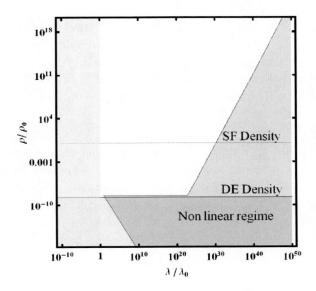

Figure 7. Similar to Figs.(3,5), the fluid density is shown as a function of the coupling parameter λ. In this scenario $\lambda_0 = 0.69$ is the comparison value [21].

In Figure 7, it is observed that for $\lambda < 0.69$ the modification to the collapse phenomenon is negligible, while for $\lambda > 0.69$ the modification becomes relevant, especially at densities close to the vacuum energy. Numerical simulations show that denser fluids are less affected by this modification [20].

Collapse in $f(R)$ gravity

For viable models of gravity to be formed in the $f(R)$ class of theories, collapse must occur at time scales much shorted than the age of the Universe. For this reason an important factor in studying gravitational collapse in these class of theories is the relative time scale that the process will take.

The particular models presented differ in their behaviors as compared with general relativity. However all give an initial curvature higher than general relativity. This fits in with the picture that $f(R)$ gravity offers since the class of gravity models can be considered as one way of adding an additional scalar field to standard general relativity [36, 47], which is always attractive in nature. Observation may be pointing toward this faster collapse rate as noted in Refs.[3, 52, 59, 37, 18] but better observations would be needed to make a more definite statement on the matter. In any case with the $f(R)$ class of gravity theories different faster collapse models can be investigated and compared against each other.

While the three models presented share these general features, they also have internal differences between each other. The $f(R) = R^2$ modification increases with density since $\Delta t_{mod}/t_{GR} \propto \sqrt{\rho}$ whereas this effect is reverse in the second model, $f(R) = R^{-1}$, where

$\Delta t_{mod}/t_{GR} \propto \rho^{-6}$. In the Starobinsky model a similar effect is observed, however this is only done numerically due to there not being an analytic solution to the governing equation for $g(\psi)$. These behaviors take hold in the nonlinear regime which is where the very interesting process characteristics are found. In Figs.(3,5,7) the regions of parameter space where the nonlinear analysis applies are shown.

As in the general relativistic case it must be kept in mind that these are indicative and not final results since the role of pressure is not studied here. Indeed pressure, while it is expected to play a minor role for most of the collapse phase, is neglected in the vast majority of theoretical collapse studies due to the complexity of the resulting equations inclusion gives. This would be one area where progression may yield some interesting and, if nothing else, new results.

Besides pressure considerations, it was shown in Ref.[98] that under certain physical conditions for the collapsing fluid, $f(R)$ gravity provides naked singularities similar to general relativity. It has to be stressed that these conditions concern the process of gravitational collapse and not processes that occur to the system once it has collapsed such as over charging the system.

IV. Collapse in Other Gravity Models

There are a plethora of gravitational theories designed to medicate the problematic parts of general relativity, in Ref.[89] most of the ones with a cosmological effect are introduced and explored. Each of these modified theories of gravity predict varying processes by which fluids collapse. However direct work on collapse predictions is lacking in a number of theories and moreover it is not clear exactly what happens during the final phases of the collapse phenomenon in these theories.

The first modification to Einstein's general relativity to be considered is the addition of the cosmological constant. For a nonzero Λ it has been shown in Ref.[79] that for a collapsing fluid with pressure $p < \Lambda/8\pi$, the cosmological constant retards the collapse. In the situation where $p > \Lambda/8\pi$ the cosmological constant term accelerates the process of collapse. For the case where the pressure vanishes, i.e., the stress-energy tensor is equal to the dust solution, Λ acts as a repulsive force and decelerates the process of collapse to singularity. Hence in the cases where the cosmological constant is allowed to be nonzero, the pressure parameter takes on the role of bounding the different possible sub-processes that take place during collapse. However more work needs to be done in the final phases of collapse and the role of Λ there.

To a lesser degree simply allowing for higher dimensions in general relativity may also give some interesting results. In [32] this scenario is investigated in Husain spacetime with a Chaplygin gas model. They find that collapse to a singularity is inevitable here as well. However the particulars of the collapse process are not determined and moreover the rate of collapse of the surface is not calculated which makes it difficult to compare the effects of adding higher dimensions to general relativity with other models of collapsing fluids.

Another example of a theory where initial work has done is found in a second generalized class of theories called *teleparallel gravity*. In general relativity the Christoffel symbols are assumed to be torsion free meaning that

$$T^\rho_{\ \nu\mu} = \Gamma^\rho_{\ \nu\mu} - \Gamma^\rho_{\ \mu\nu}, \tag{112}$$

is taken as being equal to zero. However teleparallel gravity explored the possibility of a nonvanishing torsion component to gravity where $T^\rho_{\ \nu\mu}$ is nonzero. This leads to a re-representation of the action of general relativity from its form in Eq.(1) into the form [94]

$$S_{GR} = \frac{1}{16\pi G} \int d^4x \sqrt{-g}\, T + \int d^4x \sqrt{-g}\, \mathcal{L}_M, \tag{113}$$

where

$$T = \frac{1}{4} T^{\rho\mu\nu} T_{\rho\mu\nu} + \frac{1}{2} T^{\rho\mu\nu} T_{\nu\mu\rho} - T_{\rho\mu}^{\ \ \rho} T^{\nu\mu}_{\ \ \nu}. \tag{114}$$

Doing this alone does not change the expression of gravitational theory through prediction since what it really does is exchange the curvature component of gravity with torsion [30], a generalization process is needed to make this a modified theory of gravity. Generalized teleparallel gravity is centered around the generalization of this Lagrangian to the arbitrary function $f(T)$, which is a similar approach as the $f(R)$ class of gravity models. This leads to many interesting features however a more complete review of this theory can be found in Ref.[1].

Some initial work on the study of collapsing fluids in $f(T)$ gravity has been done [81, 4]. In these works the issue of stability is studied. In particular it is shown that compact stellar objects are formed and furthermore the collapse equations through the field equations are formed. However this only covered the phase up to the formation of the stellar object. It would be interesting to investigate the process by which stellar collapse at the end of the star's life occurs, similar to the $f(R)$ case in the preceding section.

Similar to $f(T)$ theory, Einstein-Cartan theory allows for a torsion component to the gravitational model. As in the $f(T)$ case the torsion acts as a source of spin [1] while the curvature of spacetime governs the energy-momentum of the system. Looking at the Lagrangian things start to change, the modification to the Einstein gravity Lagrangian with a cosmological constant comes in the form of an additional term wholly dependent on the contorsion tensor

$$K^\mu_{\ \alpha\beta} = \frac{1}{2}\left(T^\mu_{\ \alpha\beta} - T_\alpha^{\ \mu}_{\ \beta} - T_\beta^{\ \mu}_{\ \alpha}\right), \tag{115}$$

where $T^\mu_{\ \alpha\beta}$ keeps its torsion form, as defined in Eq.(112). Additionally the metric and connection, $\Gamma^\mu_{\alpha\beta}$, are taken to be independent fields in general. The action is then taken to be [1, 43]

$$
\begin{aligned}
S &= \int d^4x \sqrt{-g}\left[-\frac{1}{\kappa^2}\left(\hat{R} + 2\Lambda\right) + \mathcal{L}_m\right] \\
&= \int d^4x \sqrt{-g}\left[-\frac{1}{\kappa^2}\left(R(\{\}) + K^\alpha_{\ \rho\alpha}K^{\rho\lambda}_{\ \ \lambda} + K^\beta_{\ \sigma\pi}K^{\sigma\pi}_{\ \ \beta} + 2\Lambda\right) + \mathcal{L}_m\right],
\end{aligned}
\tag{116}
$$

where $\hat{R}$ is the Ricci scalar as defined on the connection $\hat{\Gamma}^\alpha_{\mu\nu} = \Gamma^\alpha_{\mu\nu} + K^\alpha_{\ \mu\nu}$. The second line explicitly shows the relation of the contorsion tension in the Lagrangian. This is related through

$$\hat{R} = R(\{\}) + \nabla_\lambda K^{\lambda\rho}_{\ \ \rho} - \nabla_\rho K^{\lambda\rho}_{\ \ \lambda} + K^{\sigma\mu}_{\ \ \mu}K^\lambda_{\ \sigma\lambda} - K^{\sigma\rho}_{\ \ \nu}K^\nu_{\ \sigma\rho}. \tag{117}$$

In Ref.[97], the Weyssenhoff fluid [67] is allowed to collapse under its own gravity. This is an ideal fluid that takes into account properties of spin and torsion in the spacetime manifold [15]. In their work, Ref.[97] assumed a negative cosmological contribution and found that collapse to a singularity is not an inevitable result in such a situation. Indeed due to contributions from the spin of the background spacetime a bounce solution may occur where the singularity is avoided completely. In a second set of solutions it is also found that depending on the energy and spin of the system in question, a *locally naked singularity* may form, however this can be avoided if the right conditions are set. A naked singularity is said to be only locally naked when the weak energy condition is indeed satisfied in some segments of the spacetime. This is not the only theory to predict such a result however for a set of initial conditions the theory is very decisive giving precise results.

Another straightforward modification of the general theory of relativity is the Einstein-Gauss-Bonnet gravity model which again appears as an additional term to the Lagrangian. Here the Einstein-Hilbert Lagrangian $R - 2\Lambda$ is altered by adding a boundary term $G \equiv R^2 - 4R_{\alpha\beta}R^{\alpha\beta} + R_{\mu\nu\alpha\beta}R^{\mu\nu\alpha\beta}$ with a coupling constant α. In regular $(3+1)$ dimensional manifolds, this adds nothing to the theory since the additional terms acts like a boundary term and vanishes on variation of the action. In higher dimensions, however, the terms has a nonzero effect and alters, to varying amounts, the predictions of higher dimensional general relativity. the case of a spherically collapsing fluid is explored in Refs.[39, 95, 63, 57]. It is found that for the situation where only one extra dimension is added, i.e., $(4+1)$ −dimensions, the collapsing system must find its final state as a naked singularity. In Refs.[39, 95] it is pointed out that in this case the singularity does not feature a strong gravitational singularity and so may not pose the same threat that naked singularities normally do. That is to say that the system may not allow for a serious breach of the cosmic censorship hypothesis.

Naked singularities are also found in the Brans-Dicke gravitational theory, here a scalar field is added to general relativity such that the action is modified to [16]

$$S = \frac{1}{16\pi} \int d^4x \sqrt{-g} \left[\phi R - \frac{\omega(\phi)}{\phi} \nabla_\mu \phi \nabla^\mu \phi \right] + \int d^4x \sqrt{-g} \mathcal{L}_M \qquad (118)$$

where the scalar field is represented by ϕ and ω is the gravitational coupling constant of ϕ. Varying this with respect to both the metric tensor and the scalar field gives the following governing field equations [89]

$$\phi G_{\mu\nu} + \left[\Box\phi + \frac{1}{2}\frac{\omega}{\phi} \left(\nabla\phi\right)^2 \right] g_{\mu\nu} - \nabla_\mu\nabla_\nu\phi - \frac{\omega}{\phi}\nabla_\mu\phi\nabla_\nu\phi = 8\pi T_{\mu\nu}, \qquad (119)$$

$$\Box\phi = \frac{8\pi}{3+2\omega}T. \qquad (120)$$

In [77, 99, 26] the collapse of a barotropic fluid is explored with similar results being found. A barotropic fluid refers to a fluid whose pressure depends on its density only, in the current case the relation is linear [58]. It is found that in all cases the singularity is formed however for the cases where the coupling constant is $-\frac{1}{3}$ or $-\frac{2}{3}$, the formation of the event horizon may fail; these solutions correspond to the cosmic string and domain wall solutions. The lack of event horizon formation is confirmed by computation of the Kretschmann scalar, $\mathcal{K} \equiv R_{\mu\nu\alpha\beta}R^{\mu\nu\alpha\beta}$.

There have been a number of generalizations of Brans-Dicke theory however one interesting and very inclusive modification is the Galilean model [65]. The Galileon action is given by

$$S = \int d^4x \sqrt{-g} \left[\frac{R}{16\pi G} - \frac{1}{2} \sum_{i=1}^{5} c_i \mathcal{L}_i - \mathcal{L}_m \right], \tag{121}$$

where c_i are dimensionless coupling constants and the Lagrangian components, $\mathcal{L}_i$, are produced by the galilean style shift symmetry $\partial_\mu \phi \to \partial_\mu \phi + b_\mu$ in flat spacetime, where b_μ a constant vector. This produces the following five components

$$\mathcal{L}_1 = M^3 \phi, \tag{122}$$

$$\mathcal{L}_2 = \nabla_\mu \phi \nabla^\mu \phi, \tag{123}$$

$$\mathcal{L}_3 = \frac{2}{M^3} \Box \phi \nabla_\mu \phi \nabla^\mu \phi, \tag{124}$$

$$\mathcal{L}_4 = \frac{1}{M^6} \nabla_\mu \phi \nabla^\mu \phi \left[2 \left(\Box \phi \right)^2 - 2 \left(\nabla_\mu \nabla_\nu \phi \right) \left(\nabla^\mu \nabla^\nu \phi \right) - R \nabla_\mu \phi \nabla^\mu \phi / 2 \right], \tag{125}$$

$$\mathcal{L}_5 = \frac{1}{M^9} \nabla_\mu \phi \nabla^\mu \phi \left[\left(\Box \phi \right)^3 - 3 \left(\Box \phi \right) \left(\nabla_\mu \nabla_\nu \phi \right) \left(\nabla^\mu \nabla^\nu \phi \right) + 2 \left(\nabla_\mu \nabla^\nu \phi \right) \left(\nabla_\nu \nabla^\rho \phi \right) \left(\nabla_\rho \nabla^\mu \phi \right) \right.$$

$$\left. - 6 \left(\nabla_\mu \phi \right) \left(\nabla^\mu \nabla^\nu \phi \right) \left(\nabla^\rho \phi \right) G_{\nu\rho} \right], \tag{126}$$

where $M^3 \equiv M_{Pl} H_0^2$, M_{Pl} is the reduced Planck mass, $M_{Pl} = \sqrt{\frac{\hbar c}{8\pi G}}$, and H_0 is the present day Hubble constant. The resulting theory is systematically constrained to beng second order.

As in a number of other studies in separate theories the full collapse study is yet to be done, but initial work is under way. In Ref.[8] again the ultimate singularity fate of the collapse follows. An interesting point found is that the modified terms in the Lagrangian do in fact play a non-negligible role in the collapse process, even $\mathcal{L}_4$ and $\mathcal{L}_5$ which would be expected to not contribute significantly to the overall process. There is still work to be done in that it is not clear exactly how long this process takes in comparison to general relativity. Moreover Ref.[8] assumes a pressureless fluid, the role of pressure may have a different importance here than in general relativity. In Ref.[6], collapse is also studied however this is studied through the expression of a fifth force due to the modified terms in the Lagrangian. Here the collapse to singularity guarantee is weakened slightly. For particular values of the coupling constants c_i, the collapse solution does not remain real. It is unclear what happens in these instances, however the main result of collapse to singularity is preserved in most cases.

For some realistic constraints on the parameter space of the coupling constants some work has been in done in Ref.[7].

Neglecting the requirement of having second order field equations, the Lovelock class of generalisation of the general relativistic Lagrangian can be investigated. Here the Lagrangian is modified to [89]

$$\mathcal{L} = \sum_{n=0}^{m} \alpha_n \mathcal{L}_n, \tag{127}$$

where α_n are a set of coupling constants and $\mathcal{L}_n$ are the differently ordered Lovelock terms given by

$$\mathcal{L}_n = \frac{1}{2^n} \delta^{a_1 b_1 \cdots a_n b_n}_{c_1 b_2 \cdots c_n d_n} R^{c_1 d_1}{}_{a_1 b_1} \cdots R^{c_n d_n}{}_{a_n b_n}. \qquad (128)$$

$\delta^{a_1 b_1 \cdots a_n b_n}_{c_1 b_2 \cdots c_n d_n}$ is the generalized completely anti-symmetric Kronecker delta function. $\mathcal{L}_0$ gives a constant value with a resulting term attributed to the cosmological constant term of general relativity. $\mathcal{L}_1$ gives the Ricci scalar in the Einstein-Hilbert action. The Gauss-Bonnet term appears in $\mathcal{L}_3$. As mentioned above this term will have an effect for all but the $(3+1)-$dimensional case. A spherically symmetric solution for the theory up to third order is found in [60]. $\mathcal{L}_4$ and $\mathcal{L}_5$ represent new terms that do not feature in other formal modified theories of gravity.

In Ref.[66] the case of a collapsing dust solution, pressureless fluid, is investigated in Lovelock gravity up to third order. The main focus here is on deciphering the casual structure of the collapsed body. It was found that this depends heavily on whether the space has even or odd dimensionality. For even dimensionality regular horizon trapped singularities are allowed to form. However in the odd dimensional case, a naked singularity may form depending on the exact form of collapse present. It is expected that this feature will also appear in the full version of Lovelock gravity. In Refs.[96] the result is confirmed.

Ref.[68] studies in detail the possibility that a singularity may not occur and the shell collapse may indeed bounce at a radial position close to the gravitational center of the body. However they show that this is not possible and the collapse to singularity is indeed safe in general in Lovelock gravity. The same authors generalize their result to the charged case in Ref.[69]. However here the charge element of the collapsing shells allows for some forms of weakly charged shell collapses. This does not stop the formation of the singularity but it does alter slightly the final mass in a minor way.

Further tensor generalizations of general relativity have not yet shown much in the way of promise of a working theory where collapse can be studied however there are a number of ideas currently being developed that may give a working theory alternative to general relativity, some of these can be found in Ref.[89] but others exist in the literature as well.

On the line of scalar field modifications, chameleon field modifications to general relativity introduce a scalar field that couples to matter. This arises out of a conformal rescaling of the metric tensor. The result is a nonlinear, self-interacting particle with a variable effective mass which varies according to the surrounding ambient energy density. The particle is posed to take the role of dark energy source however experimental observation is still lacking [35]. The chameleon field is introduced in the Einstein-Hilbert action by means of the alteration below

$$S = \int d^4 x \sqrt{-g} \left[\frac{M_{Pl}^2}{2} R - \frac{1}{2} \partial_\mu \phi \partial_\nu \phi - V(\phi) \right] + \int d^4 x \sqrt{-g} \mathcal{L}_m \left(\psi_m^{(i)}, \tilde{g}_{\mu\nu} \right), \quad (129)$$

where $\psi_m^{(i)}$ represent the various matter fields present in the system. $\tilde{g}_{\mu\nu}$ is the conformally rescaled metric tensor given by [53]

$$\tilde{g}_{\mu\nu} = e^{2\beta\phi/M_{Pl}} g_{\mu\nu} \equiv \Omega^2(\psi) g_{\mu\nu}, \qquad (130)$$

β being a dimensionless constant.

Collapse in an FLRW universe is studied in Ref.[17] where the size of the collapsing regime emerged as an important deciding factor between two different processes at play.

For large collapsing regions the scalar field produces a shielding effect where any modifications to general relativity are concealed from the process. This is known as the *thin shell effect*. The shell shield does not form for small collapsing regions. Chameleon field inhomogeneous matter distributions are also commented on in Ref.[17]. However a full investigation is still lacking. It is expected that for large radii the effect will be negligible but for small radius-collapsing regions this may play an important role in deciding whether horizons form for example.

Moving onto the quantum theory side of the gravity spectrum we can start by considering Hořava-Lifshitz gravity. This model emerged as an attempt to overcome the problem of renormalization of general relativity. The essential idea is to allow for an anisotropic Lifshitz scaling between time and space in the UV limit while giving the same behaviour as general relativity in the IR limit. This may act as an intermediate theory between a full quantum theory of gravity and the Einstein general relativity currently in use. Fuller reviews of the theory can be found in Refs.[51, 83].

Ref.[44] presents a study of the collapse process in Hořava-Lifshitz gravity. Here an external observer still observes a Schwarzschild spacetime form in terms of the gravitational field, as expected. However there are a number of differences between this and the general relativistic model. Firstly in general relativity the collapsing fluid does not necessarily have to be bounded by a thin shell during the collapse process. However in Hořava-Lifshitz gravity this is necessary. Due to the local energy conservation principle in general relativity, the energy density of a collapsing dust fluid turns out to not be constant. However in this modified case the energy conservation principle is a global property of the system and so may not also be conserved locally. In this case the energy density turns out to be constant. As would be expected the modification that Hořava-Lifshitz gravity offers applies in the strong field regime where nonlinear collapse features begin to take over. It would be interesting to see what other fluids offer in the way of ultimate collapse study.

Discussion

The case of a fluid under gravitational collapse in various gravitational theories is investigated in this chapter. In brief, the collapse process starts when the balancing force of outward pressure, which keeps the inward gravitational collapse, starts to weaken. This happens naturally at the end of a stars life when the nuclear fuel is exhausted, or more accurately when further nuclear fusion cannot take place due to insufficient pressures. For low mass starts, secondary processes lead to the star's material structure breaking apart. For a white dwarf this is the Chandrasekhar limit [23] while for neutron stars this is called the TOV limit [90, 70]. These stars encompass the vast majority of end of life stars but more obviously exist such as neutron stars with more exotic cores [22] and so on. In the modified gravity regime, alterations to these mass limitations are of interest because they set a falsifiable limit over which if stars are found, and confirmed to be of a certain type, then the model can either be constrained or scrapped all together. Thus star mass and size can be used to reduce the parameter space for such theories or wipe them out all together. In this chapter there was a focus on the collapse process itself however the mass limitations set by the modified Tolman-Oppenheimer-Volkof equations are also very important studying the collapse of fluids in modified gravity.

Besides the mass of a body the rotational and charge parameters can also affect the eventual state of a collapsing body. In fact it is not the size that defines the final state of such a body but whether or not the collapse process possesses what's called a *trapped surface*. This is a surface on which any outward pointing light ray actually converges back inwards [74, 73, 9]. With this definition in hand it may be that certain collapses still do not produce a horizon but only a trapped surface as was noted for some theories in the preceding section. Once a trapped surface is formed a singularity of some sort is expected to exist in the classical theory [74] but it is not clear if this is always the case with alternatives to general relativity. The study of trapped surfaces in alternative theories is important because if a trapped surface forms and a horizon does not then violations of the cosmic censorship hypothesis which states that at most only the big bang can be a naked singularity. Violation of this hypothesize could act as a theoretical constraint on an alternative theory of gravity. However it may be that censorship is violated in the real universe and so any constraints found would only act as a selector of regions where theories are well behaved and regions where they are not.

In most of the above analysis the pressure of the fluid was assumed to be zero, however this assumption may not hold for the entire collapse process and moreover certain fluids may have different behaviours for their pressure profile during collapse. In fact ideally the fluid investigated would take the form of a general fluid with a stress-energy tensor [54]

$$T_{\mu\nu} = (\rho + P) n_\mu n_\nu + P g_{\mu\nu} + j_\mu n_\nu + j_\nu n_\mu + \pi_{\mu\nu}, \tag{131}$$

where $\rho = \rho(t, r)$ and $P = P(t, r)$. u_μ represents the four-velocity of the fluid, while the heat flux is given by j_μ and $\pi_{\mu\nu}$ represents the trace-free viscous shear tensor. It is only by using this stress-energy solution that all the facets of a general fluid collapse can be found in completion. Saying this, charge and rotation may interact differently with pressure than it does with density in that a rotating system may produce more interesting features in certain extremes of collapse.

Thus far all the collapse processes investigated have been spherical in nature which makes sense since this is the most likely collapse mode. However for theoretical consistency it would be interesting to study the possible collapse processes and what types of singularities they give rise to. Moreover in the near future it may be possible to artificially produce mini-black holes with different topologies and so it is important to understand well the gravitational collapse processes leading to these different topological black holes.

The scenario of a cylindrical collapse is explored in Refs.[61, 62] for the general relativity case. It is found that similar to the spherical scenario naked singularities do emerge depending on the initial conditions of the collapsing body. Here dust is investigated but further work could produce the same analysis for general fluids for example. More sophisticated cylindrical collapse models where anisotropic fluid dissipation effects take place can be found in Refs.[80, 45]. However these last two papers only set up the problem. The total collapse to singularity is not studied and so it is not clear whether any causality conditions are violated. It would be interesting to see how the collapse evolves in modified gravity in comparison with general relativity.

What is really needed to gain insight into real collapsing system is a study into the observational consequences that the different theories gives for the different types of collapsing materials and modes of collapse (rotation, charge of the gravitational system). The general relativistic case has been studied well [64] with many examples of fluid and system parameters being linked to the type of gravitational wave emission they produce [31].

General relativity or whatever final classical regime model of gravity emerges, this will only describe the exterior region of the black hole singularity. Collapse can give rise to trapped surfaces and even event horizons, but what is really needed for a UV complete theory of gravity is a way of explaining exactly what is happening in the so-called singularity. While general relativity breaks down here it may be that a quantum theory of gravity can give a better description of what happens at the end of collapse and how the body evolves after final collapse to a point. This is not to say there have not been interesting attempts at deciphering what happens at the point where the singularity is produced in the Einstein-Hilbert picture of gravity [91]. However due to the lack of a fundamental theory of gravity that is UV complete the discussion inevitably only gives the same evolution as the general relativity picture with the added dimension of a fuller thermodynamical treatment [48].

This is not to say that the thermodynamics of the system are not important. In fact in the semi-classical approach to the problem has given good results for eventual state of the black hole singularity however a full quantum theory of gravity would be required to study the actual singularity and its evolution. In Ref.[33] the general relativistic case of a charged black hole is investigated. They calculate the Hawking radiation for the black hole over time. This process utilizes the uncertainty in position over time to allow for the escape to infinity of particles carrying part of the black hole energy. It is shown that as the mass of the system reduces to zero, the entropy increases. Thus the end of the black hole is marked by a dark very low mass singularity with a large amount of entropy. The analysis employs the idea of a generalized uncertainty principle that also includes the contribution from gravity. This analysis is extended to other theories of gravity with varying results [55, 56, 25]. However to really understand the end of the collapse of a material body due to the gravitational field a much fully theory of gravity at small scales is needed, but for the time being much can be said about it evolution as seen by an exterior observer at infinity.

References

[1] R. Aldrovandi and J. G. Pereira. *Teleparallel Gravity: An Introduction*. Springer, Dordrecht Heidelberg New York London, 2013.

[2] L. Baiotti, I. Hawke, P. J. Montero, F. Löffler, L. Rezzolla, N. Stergioulas, J. A. Font, and E. Seidel. Three-dimensional relativistic simulations of rotating neutron-star collapse to a kerr black hole. *Phys. Rev. D*, 71:024035, 2005.

[3] M. Baldi and V. Pettorino. High-z massive clusters as a test for dynamical coupled dark energy. *Mon. Not. Roy. Astron. Soc.*, 412:L1, 2011.

[4] K. Bamba, R. Myrzakulov, S. Nojiri, and S. D. Odintsov. Reconstruction of $f(t)$ gravity: Rip cosmology, finite-time future singularities, and thermodynamics. *Phys. Rev. D*, 85:104036, 2012.

[5] K. Bamba and S. D. Odintsov. Universe acceleration in modified gravities: $F(R)$ and $F(T)$ cases. 2014.

[6] A. Barreira, B. Li, C. M. Baugh, and S. Pascoli. Spherical collapse in Galileon gravity: fifth force solutions, halo mass function and halo bias. *JCAP*, 1311:056, 2013.

[7] A. Barreira, B. Li, A. Sanchez, C. M. Baugh, and S. Pascoli. Parameter space in Galileon gravity models. *Phys. Rev. D*, 87(10):103511, 2013.

[8] E. Bellini, N. Bartolo, and S. Matarrese. Spherical Collapse in covariant Galileon theory. *JCAP*, 1206:019, 2012.

[9] Ingemar Bengtsson. Some examples of trapped surfaces. 2011.

[10] C. P. L. Berry and J. R. Gair. Linearized $f(R)$ gravity: Gravitational radiation and Solar System tests. *Phys. Rev. D*, 83:104022, 2011.

[11] G. Bertone. *Particle Dark Matter: Observations, Models and Searches* . Cambridge University Press, 2010.

[12] G. Bertone, D. Hooper, and J. Silk. Particle dark matter: Evidence, candidates and constraints. *Phys. Rept.*, 405:279–390, 2005.

[13] J. Bičák and T. Ledvinka. *General Relativity, Cosmology and Astrophysics: Perspectives 100 Years After Einstein's Stay in Prague* . Fundamental Theories of Physics. Springer International Publishing, 2014.

[14] G.D. Birkhoff and R.E. Langer. *Relativity and Modern Physics* . Harvard University Press, 1923.

[15] C. G. Boehmer and P. Bronowski. The Homogeneous and isotropic Weyssenhoff fluid. *Ukr. J. Phys.*, 55:607–612, 2010.

[16] C. Brans and R. H. Dicke. Mach's principle and a relativistic theory of gravitation. *Phys. Rev.*, 124:925–935, 1961.

[17] Ph. Brax, R. Rosenfeld, and D.A. Steer. Spherical Collapse in Chameleon Models. *JCAP*, 1008:033, 2010.

[18] M. Brodwin, J. Ruel, P.A.R. Ade, K.A. Aird, K. Andersson, et al. SPT-CL J0546-5345: A Massive z > 1 Galaxy Cluster Selected Via the Sunyaev-Zel'dovich Effect with the South Pole Telescope. *Astrophys.J.*, 721:90–97, 2010.

[19] S. M. Carroll, V. Duvvuri, M. Trodden, and M. S. Turner. Is cosmic speed-up due to new gravitational physics? *Phys. Rev. D*, 70:043528, 2004.

[20] de la Cruz-Dombriz A. Cembranos, J. A. R. and B. Montes Núñez. Gravitational collapse in f(R) theories. *Journal of Cosmology and Astroparticle Physics* , 04:021, 2012.

[21] J. A. R. Cembranos. Dark Matter from R^2 Gravity. *Phys. Rev. Lett.*, 102:141301, 2009.

[22] N. Chamel, A.F. Fantina, J.M. Pearson, and S. Goriely. Maximum mass of neutron stars with exotic cores. *Astron. Astrophys.*, 553:A22, 2013.

[23] S. Chandrasekhar. *Astronomical Journal*, 74:81, 1931.

[24] S. Chandrasekhar. *The Mathematical Theory of Black Holes*. Oxford University Press, New York, 1983.

[25] De-You Chen, Qing-Quan Jiang, Shu-Zheng Yang, and Xiao-Tao Zu. Fermions tunnelling from the charged dilatonic black holes. *Class. Quant. Grav.*, 25:205022, 2008.

[26] T. Chiba and J. Soda. Critical behavior in the Brans-Dicke theory of gravitation. *Prog. Theor. Phys.*, 96:567–574, 1996.

[27] T. Clifton. The Parameterised Post-Newtonian Limit of Fourth-Order Theories of Gravity. *Phys. Rev. D*, 77:024041, 2008.

[28] J. M. Cohen. Gravitational collapse of rotating bodies. *Phys. Rev.*, 173:1258–1263, 1968.

[29] De-C. Dai, I. Maor, and G. Starkman. Consequences of the absence of birkhoff's theorem in modified-gravity theories: The dvali-gabadaze-porrati model. *Phys. Rev. D*, 77:064016, 2008.

[30] V.C. De Andrade, L.C.T. Guillen, and J.G. Pereira. *Teleparallel gravity: An Overview*, 2000.

[31] C. de Witt and International Astronomical Union. *Gravitational Radiation and Gravitational Collapse*. IAU symposium. Springer Netherlands, 1974.

[32] Ujjal Debnath, Narayan Chandra Chakraborty, and Subenoy Chakraborty. Gravitational Collapse in Higher Dimensional Husain Space-Time. *Gen. Rel. Grav.*, 40:749–763, 2008.

[33] M. Dehghani and A. Farmany. GUP and higher dimensional Reissner-Nordstr Ãm black hole radiation. *Brazilian Journal of Physics*, 39:570–573, 2009.

[34] B. S. DeWitt. *Relativity, Groups and Topology*. Gordon and Breach, New York, 1964.

[35] A. L. Erickcek, N. Barnaby, C. Burrage, and Z. Huang. Catastrophic Consequences of Kicking the Chameleon. *Phys. Rev. Lett.*, 110:171101, 2013.

[36] Antonio De F. and Shinji T. f(r) theories. *Living Reviews in Relativity*, 13(3), 2010.

[37] R.J. Foley, K. Andersson, G. Bazin, T. de Haan, J. Ruel, et al. Discovery and Cosmological Implications of SPT-CL J2106-5844, the Most Massive Known Cluster at z > 1. *Astrophys. J.*, 731:86, 2011.

[38] A. Ganguly, R. Gannouji, R. Goswami, and S. Ray. Neutron stars in Starobinsky model. *Phys. Rev. D.*, 89:064019, 2014.

[39] S. G. Ghosh, S. Jhingan, and D.W. Deshkar. Spherical gravitational collapse in 5D Einstein-Gauss-Bonnet gravity. *J. Phys. Conf. Ser.*, 484:012013, 2014.

[40] K. Giesel, S. Hofmann, T. Thiemann, and O. Winkler. Manifestly Gauge-invariant general relativistic perturbation theory. II. FRW background and first order. *Class.Quant.Grav.*, 27:055006, 2010.

[41] K. Giesel and T. Thiemann. Algebraic Quantum Gravity (AQG). I. Conceptual Setup. *Class.Quant.Grav.*, 24:2465–2498, 2007.

[42] K. Giesel and T. Thiemann. Algebraic quantum gravity (AQG). III. Semiclassical perturbation theory. *Class.Quant.Grav.*, 24:2565–2588, 2007.

[43] Hubert F. M. Goenner. On the history of unified field theories. *Living Reviews in Relativity*, 7(2), 2004.

[44] Jared Greenwald, Jonatan Lenells, V.H. Satheeshkumar, and Anzhong Wang. Gravitational collapse in Hořava-Lifshitz theory. *Phys. Rev. D*, 88(2):024044, 2013.

[45] S. Guha and R. Banerji. Dissipative cylindrical collapse of charged anisotropic fluid. *International Journal of Theoretical Physics*, 53(7):2332–2348, 2014.

[46] I. Hachisu, M. Kato, H. Saio, and K. Nomoto. A single degenerate progenitor model for type ia supernovae highly exceeding the chandrasekhar mass limit. *The Astrophysical Journal*, 744(1):69, 2012.

[47] T. Harko, F. S. N. Lobo, and O. Minazzoli. Extended $f(r, L_m)$ gravity with generalized scalar field and kinetic term dependences. *Phys. Rev. D*, 87:047501, 2013.

[48] S.W. Hawking. Particle Creation by Black Holes. *Commun. Math. Phys.*, 43:199–220, 1975.

[49] S.W. Hawking and W. Israel. *General Relativity: An Einstein Centenary Survey*. Cambridge University Press, 1979.

[50] M. P. Hobson, G. P. Efstathiou, and A. N. Lasenby. *General Relativity: An Introduction for Physicists*. Cambridge University Press, 2006.

[51] Petr Horava. Quantum Gravity at a Lifshitz Point. *Phys.Rev.*, D79:084008, 2009.

[52] M.J. Jee, P. Rosati, H.C. Ford, K.S. Dawson, C. Lidman, et al. Hubble Space Telescope Weak-lensing Study of the Galaxy Cluster XMMU J2235.3-2557 at z=1.4: A Surprisingly Massive Galaxy Cluster when the Universe is One-third of its Current Age. *Astrophys.J.*, 704:672–686, 2009.

[53] J. Khoury and A. Weltman. Chameleon fields: Awaiting surprises for tests of gravity in space. *Phys. Rev. Lett.*, 93:171104, 2004.

[54] Paul D. Lasky and Anthony W.C. Lun. Spherically Symmetric Gravitational Collapse of General Fluids. *Phys. Rev. D*, 75:024031, 2007.

[55] J. Levi Said and K. Zarb Adami. Generalized uncertainty principle in $f(r)$ gravity for a charged black hole. *Phys. Rev. D*, 83:043008, 2011.

[56] Cheng-Zhou Liu. Hawking radiation via tunneling of massive particles from a gravity's rainbow. *Mod.Phys.Lett.*, A25:3229–3240, 2010.

[57] Hideki Maeda. Effects of Gauss-Bonnet terms on final fate of gravitational collapse. *Class. Quant. Grav.*, 23:2155, 2006.

[58] C. W. Misner, K. S. Thorne, and J. A. Wheeler. *Gravitation*. W. H. Freeman, 1973.

[59] M. J. Mortonson, W. Hu, and D. Huterer. Simultaneous Falsification of ΛCDM and Quintessence with Massive, Distant Clusters. *Phys. Rev. D*, 83:023015, 2011.

[60] R. C. Myers and J. Z. Simon. Black Hole Evaporation and Higher Derivative Gravity. *Gen. Rel. Grav.*, 21:761–766, 1989.

[61] K. Nakao, Y. Kurita, Y. Morisawa, and T. Harada. Relativistic Gravitational Collapse of a Cylindrical Shell of Dust. *Prog. Theor. Phys.*, 117:75–102, 2007.

[62] Ken-ichi Nakao, Tomohiro Harada, Yasunari Kurita, and Yoshiyuki Morisawa. Relativistic Gravitational Collapse of a Cylindrical Shell of Dust II: Settling Down Boundary Condition. *Prog. Theor. Phys.*, 122:521–541, 2009.

[63] M. Narita. On spherically symmetric gravitational collapse in the Einstein-Gauss-Bonnet theory. *AIP Conf. Proc.*, 1122:356–359, 2009.

[64] Kimberly C.B. New. Gravitational waves from gravitational collapse. *Living Rev. Rel.*, 6:2, 2003.

[65] A. Nicolis, R. Rattazzi, and E. Trincherini. The Galileon as a local modification of gravity. *Phys. Rev. D*, 79:064036, 2009.

[66] M. Nozawa and H. Maeda. Effects of lovelock terms on the final fate of gravitational collapse: Analysis in dimensionally continued gravity. *Class. Quant. Grav.*, 23:1779–1800, 2006.

[67] Y.N. Obukhov and V.A. Korotkii. The Weyssenhoff fluid in Einstein-Cartan theory. *Class. Quant. Grav.*, 4:1633–1657, 1987.

[68] S. Ohashi, T. Shiromizu, and S. Jhingan. Spherical collapse of inhomogeneous dust cloud in the Lovelock theory. *Phys. Rev. D*, 84:024021, 2011.

[69] S. Ohashi, T. Shiromizu, and S. Jhingan. Gravitational collapse of charged dust cloud in the Lovelock gravity. *Phys. Rev. D*, 86:044008, 2012.

[70] J. R. Oppenheimer and G. M. Volkoff. On massive neutron cores. *Phys. Rev.*, 55:374–381, 1939.

[71] Oregon. Pie chart display of the energy budget of the universe.
http://abyss.uoregon.edu/ js/21st _century_science/lectures/lec23.html, 2013.

[72] C. D. Ott, H. Dimmelmeier, A. Marek, H.-T. Janka, I. Hawke, et al. 3D Collapse
of Rotating Stellar Iron Cores in General Relativity with Microphysics. *Phys. Rev. Lett.*, 98:261101, 2007.

[73] R. Penrose. Gravitational collapse and space-time singularities. *Phys. Rev. Lett.*, 14:57–59, 1965.

[74] R. Penrose. Gravitational collapse: The role of general relativity. *Riv.Nuovo Cim.*, 1:252–276, 1969.

[75] A. Riess. *Astronomical Journal*, 116:1009, 1998.

[76] W. Rindler. *Relativity: Special, General, and Cosmological*. Oxford University
Press, 2006.

[77] P. Rudra, R. Biswas, and U. Debnath. Gravitational Collapse In Husain Space-time
For Brans-Dicke Gravity Theory. 2013.

[78] K. Schleich and D. M. Witt. A simple proof of birkhoff's theorem for cosmological
constant. *Journal of Mathematical Physics*, 51(11):–, 2010.

[79] M. Sharif and Z. Ahmad. Gravitational Perfect Fluid Collapse With Cosmological
Constant. *Mod. Phys. Lett.*, A22:1493–1502, 2007.

[80] M. Sharif and Sundas Fatima. Charged Cylindrical Collapse of Anisotropic Fluid.
Gen. Rel. Grav., 43:127–142, 2011.

[81] M. Sharif and S. Rani. Dynamical instability of spherical collapse in f(T) gravity.
Mon. Not. Roy. Astron. Soc., 440(3):2255–2264, 2014.

[82] M. Shibata. Axisymmetric Simulations of Rotating Stellar Collapse in Full General Relativity: Criteria for Prompt Collapse to Black Holes. *Prog. Theor. Phys.*, 104:325–358, 2000.

[83] T. P. Sotiriou. Horava-Lifshitz gravity: a status report. *J.Phys.Conf.Ser.*, 283:012034, 2011.

[84] T. P. Sotiriou and V. Faraoni. f(R) theories of gravity. *Rev. Mod. Phys.*, 82:451–497, 2010.

[85] A. A. Starobinsky. A new type of isotropic cosmological models without singularity.
Phys. Lett. B, 91:99–102, 1980.

[86] A. A. Starobinsky. *JETP Lett.*, 86:157, 2007.

[87] Nikolaos Stergioulas. Rotating stars in relativity. *Living Reviews in Relativity*, 6(3), 2003.

[88] I. Thongkool, M. Sami, and S. R. Choudhury. How delicate are the f(R) gravity models with disappearing cosmological constant? *Phys. Rev. D.*, 80:127501, 2009.

[89] C. Timothy, G. F. Pedro, P. Antonio, and S. Constantinos. Modified gravity and cosmology. *Physics Reports*, 513(13):1–189, 2012.

[90] R. C. Tolman. Static solutions of einstein's field equations for spheres of fluid. *Phys. Rev.*, 55:364–373, 1939.

[91] C. Vaz and L. Witten. Canonical quantization of spherically symmetric dust collapse. *Gen. Rel. Grav.*, 43:3429–3449, 2011.

[92] R. M. Wald. *General Relativity*. The University of Chicago Press, Chicago and London, 1984.

[93] S. Weinberg. *Gravitation and Cosmology: Principles and Applications of the General Theory of Relativity*. John Wiley & Sons Inc., New York, 1972.

[94] Rong-Jia Y. Conformal transformation in f(t) theories. *EPL (Europhysics Letters)*, 93(6):60001, 2011.

[95] K. Zhou, Zhan-Y. Yang, De-C. Zou, and Rui-H. Yue. Spherically symmetric gravitational collapse of a dust cloud in Einstein-Gauss-Bonnet Gravity. *Mod. Phys. Lett.*, A26:2135–2147, 2011.

[96] Kang Zhou, Zhan-Ying Yang, De-Cheng Zou, and Rui-Hong Yue. Spherically symmetric gravitational collapse of a dust cloud in third order Lovelock Gravity. *Int. J. Mod. Phys.*, D20:2317–2335, 2011.

[97] A. H. Ziaie, P. V. Moniz, A. Ranjbar, and H. R. Sepangi. Einstein-Cartan gravitational collapse of a homogeneous Weyssenhoff fluid. 2013.

[98] A.H. Ziaie, K. Atazadeh, and S.M.M. Rasouli. Naked Singularity Formation In f(R) Gravity. *Gen. Rel. Grav.*, 43:2943–2963, 2011.

[99] Amir Hadi Ziaie, Khedmat Atazadeh, and Yaser Tavakoli. Naked Singularity Formation In Brans-Dicke Theory. *Class. Quant. Grav.*, 27:075016, 2010.

[100] F. Zwicky. On the Masses of Nebulae and of Clusters of Nebulae. *Astrophys.J.*, 86:217–246, 1937.

In: Advances in Black Holes Research
Editor: Abraham Barton

ISBN: 978-1-63463-168-6
© 2015 Nova Science Publishers, Inc.

Chapter 5

OBSERVATIONAL LIMITS
ON MODERN EXTENDED GRAVITY MODELS

S. O. Alexeyev[1], *K. A. Rannu*[1], *P. I. Dyadina*[2] *and B. N. Latosh*[3]

[1]Sternberg Astronomical Institute of Lomonosov Moscow State University,
Universitetsky Prospekt, Moscow, Russia
[2]Department of Astrophysics and Stellar Astronomy,
Physics Faculty of Lomonosov Moscow State University,
Vorobievi Gori, Moscow, Russia
[3]Physics department Institute of Natural Science of Ural Federal University,
Yekaterinburg, Russia

Abstract

We present the ideas and some results (negative) on the experimental search for
new physics from the Gauss-Bonnet and Randall-Sundrum gravities. The idea is to
compare the anticipated experimental signals with the accuracy of modern gravitational experiments in our solar system and some cosmological tests. As a result is it
shown that the real search of the Gauss-Bonnet and Randall-Sundrum theories' predictions requires the increase of experimental accuracy.

1. Introduction

A four-dimensional low-energy effective limit of the string theory may provide important
clues on gravity quantization [1, 2]. If the string theory represents an unified limit for all
physical interactions (including gravity), the first order term of such an expansion would
be provided by the general theory of relativity (GR), while the higher-order corrections
are represented by power series respectively the scalar curvature. These terms could lead
to observable effects alerting the presence of new physics. The second order curvature
correction given by a Gauss-Bonnet term [3] coupled to the scalar (dilatonic) field [1, 2, 4,
5, 6, 7, 8] is largest and the most studied one. Such gravity models with additional scalar
fields and correction terms were used for regularizing GR [9] and attempting to incorporate
quantum effects into gravitational theory [10].

Recently four-dimensional models of gravity with non-compact extra dimensions have
also demonstrated a significant progress. The most important step was made by Randall

and Sundrum [13, 14]. They proposed that an additional dimension that is not compact could exist and, so, constructed two models of branes with tension embedded into a five-dimensional bulk space-time with an AdS_5 geometry. In their first model (RSI) [13] one of the branes has positive tension. All the matter and the three physical interactions are localized on this brane except gravity which is allowed to propagate into the bulk (along the additional non-compact dimension). The second brane (called, the TeV brane) has negative tension. Moving the second brane to the infinity leads to the Randall-Sundrum II (RSII) model (with one brane) [14]. Randall and Sundrum have demonstrated that an infinite 5th physical dimension could exist without violating constants imposed by modern gravitational experiments. This means that an extra dimension should not necessarily be a compact one and could be an infinite. The AdS_5/CFT_4 correspondence has been applied for the considerations of the RS-models and appeared to be a very useful calculation instrument. In this approach the AdS_5 bulk has the boundary value of fields that are interpreted as sources for operators of the dual conformal field theory (CFT) [15]. The effective four-dimensional theory in RS-models represents the low energy limit of the five-dimensional field equations and does not differ from the usual Newton's law on small scales.

The framework of Randall-Sundrum model yielded few types of new black holes solutions [16, 17, 18]. These solutions represent a five-dimensional "black string" intersecting with the brane in an asymptotically-Schwarzschild solution. The solution contains the additional corrections determined by the model parameters (i.e., the bulk cosmological constant and the brane tidal charge) [16, 19]. A remarkable conjecture was proposed in Refs. [20, 21, 22]: static black holes cannot exist in RSII with a radius much greater than the AdS length ℓ (although we note that this is based on free field theory intuition, which may not hold [23, 24]). Using numerical methods [25, 26] black holes in five-dimensional RSII model with a radius up to $\sim 0.2\ell$ and in six-dimensional RSII up to $\sim 2.0\ell$ were obtained [35]. However, it was argued [30, 31] that very small RSII static black holes do not exist. Contrary to this, such black hole solutions for the RSII model recently have been found [32, 33, 35]. We would like to point out that the existence of the astrophysical black holes in the theory is an important indicator of its viability. Therefore, it is important to find evidence for the bulk's influence using existing astronomical data [36, 37].

As a result of the recent efforts above, there is a number of gravitational theories that are currently viable and describe the space-time in drastically different ways, relying on new physics mechanisms that may be tested in experiment; here explore such possibilities (mostly following our recent paper [37]).

The outline of this paper is as follows: in Section 2 we discuss the weak field and slow motion approximation of the Gauss-Bonnet and Randall-Sundrum theories as the most representative examples of gravity augmentation. Section 3 is devoted to the analysis of thermodynamical properties of these models and their influence on the primordial black holes mass spectra. In Section 4 we discuss the results and give the conclusions.

2. Weak Field Limit

To consider the dynamical conditions in the solar system we use the weak field and slow motion approximation (i.e., post-Newtonian (PN) approximation) of a metric tensor, $g_{\mu\nu}$, representing the space-time produced by a static spherically-symmetric distribution of matter. Gravitational field, $h_{\mu\nu}$, is treated as a perturbation of the Minkowski space-time $\eta_{\mu\nu}$:

$$g_{\mu\nu} = \eta_{\mu\nu} + h_{\mu\nu}. \tag{1}$$

We consider only a static monopole gravity field at the distance r from an extended source. In the first PN (1PN) order, the gravitational field $h_{\mu\nu}$ is given by the expression up to the following order terms:

$$h_{00} \sim \mathcal{O}(r^{-2}), \quad h_{0j} \sim \mathcal{O}(r^{-3}), \quad h_{ij} \sim \mathcal{O}(r^{-1}), \tag{2}$$

where we use geometric units, $\hbar = c = G = 1$, with non-dimensional masses expressed in units of Plank mass. The expansion (2) is well tested by experiments [38, 36]. As experimental accuracy permanently improves [36], there may open possibilities to test small gravitational effects predicted by currently viable theories. We use the expansion (2) to compare the magnitudes of the predicted effects.

2.1. Gauss-Bonnet Gravity

Following our original paper [37] we start from the weak field limit exploration of the Gauss-Bonnet theory that describes a non-minimal coupling of the dilatonic field with gravity and other fields [1, 2, 4, 7, 8]. In the four-dimensional case this model is invariant, ghost-free and represents a low energy limit of string gravity [1, 2]:

$$S = \frac{1}{16\pi} \int d^4x \sqrt{-g} \Big[- R + 2\partial_\mu \phi \partial^\mu \phi + \lambda e^{-2\phi} S_{GB} + \dots \Big], \tag{3}$$

where ϕ is the dilatonic field, $S_{GB} = R_{ijkl} R^{ijkl} - 4R_{ij} R^{ij} + R^2$ is the Gauss-Bonnet term and λ is the string coupling constant. The aim is to construct 1PN of a static, asymptotically flat and spherically-symmetric (i.e., Schwarzschild-like) Gauss-Bonnet solution.

To identify the effects from new physics, we explore Schwarzschild-like solution for Gauss-Bonnet theory. A static, uncharged, non-rotating Schwarzschild black hole metric also serves as a good approximation for problems dealing with gravitational dynamics with a massive object in the center (i.e., our solar system). This motivates one to consider an extension to the Schwarzschild-Gauss-Bonnet solution [1, 2], so, the limits on the higher order curvature corrections (and also dynamical dilatonic) contributions can be described with the help of metric given as

$$ds^2 = \Delta dt^2 - \Delta^{-1} \sigma^2 dr^2 - r^2 \Big(d\theta^2 + \sin^2 \theta d\varphi^2 \Big), \tag{4}$$

where (t, r, θ, φ) are usual spherical coordinates. The metric functions Δ and σ depend only upon the radial coordinate r. The numerical non-perturbative solutions with nontrivial dilatonic "hair" that we use here were presented in [1, 2]. They are characterized by Arnowitt-Deser-Misner (ADM) mass M, dilatonic charge D and asymptotic value of dilatonic potential ϕ_∞. Asymptotic behavior for $r \to \infty$ is [1, 2]:

$$
\begin{aligned}
\Delta &= 1 - \frac{2M}{r} + \mathcal{O}\left(r^{-2}\right), \\
\sigma &= 1 + \mathcal{O}\left(r^{-2}\right), \\
\phi &= \phi_\infty + \frac{D}{r} + \mathcal{O}\left(r^{-2}\right),
\end{aligned} \tag{5}
$$

where $D \propto 1/M$ according to [7]. We look for a solution in the form of expansions consistent with the 1PN-order one (2).

The most convenient form of the field equations is [39]:

$$G_{\mu\nu} = 8\pi \left(T_{\mu\nu}^m + T_{\mu\nu}^\phi + T_{\mu\nu}^{\mathrm{GB}} \right), \tag{6}$$

where $T_{\mu\nu}^m$ is a stress-energy tensor of matter inside the body, while $T_{\mu\nu}^\phi$ and $T_{\mu\nu}^{\mathrm{GB}}$ are given by

$$
\begin{aligned}
T_{\mu\nu}^\phi &= \frac{1}{8\pi} \left(\partial_\mu \phi \, \partial_\nu \phi - \frac{1}{2} g_{\mu\nu} \partial^\rho \phi \, \partial_\rho \phi \right), \\
T_{\mu\nu}^{\mathrm{GB}} &= \frac{1}{8\pi} \Big[(\nabla_\mu \nabla_\nu - g_{\mu\nu} \Box)(e^{-2\phi} R) \\
&\quad + \ 2 \, (\Box \delta_\mu^\sigma \delta_\nu^\sigma + g_{\mu\nu} \nabla^\rho \nabla^\sigma - \nabla^\rho \nabla_{(\mu} \delta_{\nu)}^\sigma)(e^{-2\phi} R_{\rho\sigma}) \\
&\quad - \ 2 \nabla^\rho \nabla^\sigma (e^{-2\phi} R_{\mu\rho\nu\sigma}) \Big].
\end{aligned}
$$

Using the standard computational techniques [38] (i.e., putting metric (4) with the expansions (5) to the field equations (6)), one obtains the Gauss-Bonnet correction for the metric tensor (the leading order term is h_{00}, h_{0j} and h_{ij} are proportional to the next perturbative orders):

$$\delta h_{00}^{\mathrm{GB}} = 8 \frac{DM}{r^4} + \mathcal{O}(r^{-5}). \tag{7}$$

Contrasting this result to (2), one concludes that the correction term (7) lies beyond the 1PN order and, thus, may not be constrained by solar system tests at a present time. This result is same as in [39] where the cosmological limit of the discussed model was studied.

It is necessary to point out that in the static spherically-symmetric case the scalar field's contribution vanishes because of the Wheeler's "no-hair" theorem [40], therefore the second order curvature correction in the low-energy string gravity action does not affect the behavior of stellar system at the 1PN order.

2.2. Randall-Sundrum Gravity

2.2.1. Arguments from PPN Formalism

We switch to black hole solutions in the Randall-Sundrum model. Recently the low energy solution of the RSII model connected with an associated five-dimensional anti-de Sitter space (AdS$_5$) and AdS$_5$–CFT$_4$ correspondence was found by Figueras and Wiseman [32]. Therefore, such RSII black hole solution represents a perturbation of the AdS$_5$–CFT$_4$ one. The ratio of curvature radius of the brane metric divided to the AdS length ℓ is chosen as the perturbation parameter because of its smallness. Thus, the brane metric is a specific perturbation of the AdS$_5$–CFT$_4$ boundary one. In the low curvature limit the RSII solution transforms to a four-dimensional GR one on the brane. Figueras and Wiseman [32] modified the boundary conditions to construct large RSII static black hole with radius up to $\sim 20\ell$. The solution was obtained numerically. In the case of a large radius the RSII solutions are closely associated to the AdS_5–CFT_4 ones.

The five-dimensional metric g_{AB} obeying $R_{AB} = -(4/l^2)g_{AB}$ can be represented near the conformal boundary $z = 0$ as:

$$ds^2 = \frac{l^2}{z^2} \left[dz^2 + \tilde{g}_{\mu\nu}(z, x)\, dx^\mu dx^\nu \right], \tag{8}$$

where z is a coordinate of an extra dimension. Latin and Greek indexes denote the five-dimensional and the four-dimensional coordinates respectively, i.e., $A, B \in [0, 4]$, $\mu, \nu \in [0, 3]$. With the help of the Fefferman-Graham expansion [15] and the equations (6) from [32] one calculates the 1PN solution. This solution is valid in RSII neighborhood of $\epsilon = 0$, where parameter ϵ is the deviation of the brane position from the equilibrium. So, the additional CFT_4-term in the PN metric expansion is:

$$\delta h_{00}^{\mathrm{FW}} = \frac{\epsilon^2}{l^2} \frac{121}{27} \frac{M^2}{r^2}. \tag{9}$$

The obtained value (9) displays the contribution of the Figueras and Wiseman solution to the PN metric (2) and represents a potentially observable effect! To calculate the order of its numerical value, the result (9) has to be rewritten as the parameterized post-Newtonian (PPN) parameter β [38, 36] as follows:

$$\beta = 1 - \frac{\epsilon^2}{l^2} \frac{121}{108} M^2. \tag{10}$$

Hence, the bulk presence leads to the negative non-linearity in gravitational superposition as it was firstly shown in [37]. Therefore, in the discussed model the resulting gravitational field from two or more objects is less than their direct vector sum because gravity propagates also to the bulk. Hence, it seems possible to be able to measure the bulks' presence!

The error limitation on the PPN parameter β in the form $|\beta - 1| \leq 1.1 \times 10^{-4}$ was obtained from the lunar laser ranging data [36]. Further, the allowed region of the AdS length is limited by the experimental results on the Newton's law measuring and must be of the order of $l < 10^{-5}$ m [34]. With the help of the experimental limit on β one estimates a bound on ϵ:

$$\frac{121}{108} \frac{\epsilon^2}{l^2} M^2 \leq 1.1 \times 10^{-4}, \tag{11}$$

here M is the solar mass. Hence, the upper limit on the value of ϵ is:

$$\epsilon \leq 5.7 \times 10^{-47} \ll m_{Pl}. \tag{12}$$

From the beginning the parameter ϵ was assumed to be extremely small and the vanishing value found in (12) indicates that $\epsilon = 0$. So, the Figueras-Wiseman four-dimensional black hole solution is not only self-consistent, but it is also consistent with the solar system constraints. Therefore, the discussed model is also indistinguishable form GR at the 1PN level of accuracy.

The next RSII for a large static black hole solution was recently obtained by Abdol-rahimi, Page et al. [35] using a novel numerical spectral method of perturbing a numerical AdS$_5$–CFT$_4$ solution of the GR equations. The obtained metric is asymptotically conformal to the Schwarzschild one and includes a negative five-dimensional cosmological constant Λ_5:

$$ds^2 = -u(r)dt^2 + \frac{v(r)}{u(r)}dr^2 + \left[r^2 + \frac{F_{AP}(r)}{-\Lambda_5} \right] d\Omega^2, \tag{13}$$

where

$$u(r) \;=\; 1 - 2M/r,$$
$$v(r) \;=\; 1 + \left(\frac{r - 2M}{r - \frac{3}{2}M} \right) \left[\frac{F_{AP}(r)}{-\Lambda_5 r} \right]',$$

where $' \equiv d/dr$ is the derivative with respect to r. The factor F_{AP} is approximated to a sufficient accuracy as [35]:

$$F_{AP}(r) = 1 - 1.1241\left(2M/r\right) + 1.956\left(2M/r\right)^2 + \mathcal{O}\left(r^{-3}\right).$$

The brane field equations are derived by Shiromizu et al. [41] using the Gauss-Codazzi equations with respect to matching conditions and Z_2 symmetry. The result represents a modification of the standard Einstein equations with the corrections that carry bulk effects onto the brane:

$$G_{\mu\nu} \;=\; -\Lambda_4 g_{\mu\nu} + \frac{8\pi}{M_{P14}^2} T_{\mu\nu} + \frac{8\pi}{M_{P15}^3} S_{\mu\nu} - \mathcal{E}_{\mu\nu}, \tag{14}$$

where Λ_4 is usual cosmological constant in four dimensions, $g_{\mu\nu}$ is the metric on the brane described by expressions (13), $T_{\mu\nu}$ is the stress-energy tensor of the matter on the brane (assumed to be the perfect fluid), $S_{\mu\nu}$ is the local quadratic stress-energy correction, $\mathcal{E}_{\mu\nu}$ is the four-dimensional projection of the five-dimensional Weyl tensor. M_{P15} is the fundamental five-dimensional Planck mass, which is much less in comparison with the effective Planck one on the brane. The bulk corrections to the GR equations are non-local effects from the free gravitational field in the bulk, transmitted via projection $\mathcal{E}_{\mu\nu}$ of the bulk Weyl tensor.

Ref. [35] calculated the best fit for F_{AP} that describes the bulk caused perturbation. The induced metric on the brane appears to be flat, and the bulk is anti-de-Sitter, as in the original Randall-Sundrum scenario [14], so, $\mathcal{E}_{\mu\nu} = 0$ [17]. From (13) the correction term to 1PN order from (14) has the from:

$$\delta h_{00}^{AP} = \frac{l^2 M^2}{96} \frac{1}{r^4} + \mathcal{O}(r^{-5}). \tag{15}$$

As it was pointed out earlier the contribution to 1PN-order has the order of r^{-2}, i.e., similarly to the discussion of (7). The obtained correction (15) has the next perturbation order which is beyond 1PN. Therefore, as in the case of the Gauss-Bonnet term, the obtained contribution is less than the 1PN one and, thus, it cannot be tested in the solar system with the existing experimental accuracy. Conclusion on the model predictions is the same as in the Gauss-Bonnet and Figueras-Wiseman cases.

2.2.2. Arguments from Geodesics Lines Analysis

Another way that may lead to experimental check of extended gravity is searching for orbital effects. The classical results on orbital effects in GR [50] show that the critical value of angular momentum does exist. If particle moves near a Schwarzschild black hole with an angular momentum smaller, than the critical value, it has now any stable orbit. Comparing the value of critical angular momentum in extended gravity with the one in GR it is possible to find a difference and search for new orbits absent in GR.

Classical results [50] show, that a particle moving near a black hole with metric

$$ds^2 = A(r)dt^2 - \frac{dr^2}{B(r)} - f(r)\left(d\theta^2 + \sin^2\theta d\varphi^2\right) \tag{16}$$

has angular momentum and energy that are conserved. Thus one may consider only one-dimensional problem for particle moving in a field with a potential V:

$$V = A(r)\left(1 + \frac{L^2}{f(r)}\right), \tag{17}$$

where L is a value of angular momentum normalised on the unit mass.

For a Schwarzschild black hole equation (17) has the following form:

$$V = \left(1 - \frac{2GM}{r}\right)\left(1 + \frac{L^2}{r^2}\right). \tag{18}$$

The potential (18) has only one global maximum generating a potential barrier around black hole. Nevertheless, such a maximum exists if and only if the angular momentum is bigger than

$$L_c = \sqrt{12}GM. \tag{19}$$

If angular momentum is smaller than L_c potential (17) has no extremum and becomes infinitely deep potential well.

Coming back to Figueras and Wiseman solution [32] potential (17) has following form:

$$V = \left(1 - \frac{2GM}{r}\right)\left(1 + \frac{L^2}{r^2 + \left(\frac{l}{\sqrt{6}}\right)^2 F_{AP}}\right), \tag{20}$$

where F_{AP} is defined in Eq. ((13)). As we work with orbital effects we may assume that the black hole is macroscopic and, therefore, l is a small parameter. With such an assumption it is possible to expand Eqs (20) to the series with respect to the small parameter l and, further, to neglect the terms $\mathcal{O}(l^2)$. We neglect $\mathcal{O}(r^{-4})$ terms also because the potential V for GR ((18)) acts like $\mathcal{O}(r^{-3})$ and we leave the terms decreasing slower. After such approximations the expression for Figueras and Wiseman solution transforms to:

$$V = \left(1 - \frac{2GM}{r}\right)\left(1 + \frac{L^2}{r^2}\right) - \frac{l^2 L^2}{6\,r^4}. \tag{21}$$

From Eq. ((21)) it is seen that the main part of correction makes extremely small contribution to the potential. There is no contribution that is lineal relatively l. So, the correction decreases faster than the main GR potential and the influence of correction could be significant only at the Plank scales.

Nevertheless, it is possible to find correction to the critical angular momentum. This correction defines the scales on which one could observe the difference between Schwarzschild solution and Figueras-Wiseman one. For the potential ((21)) the value of critical momentum L_c has the form:

$$L_c = \sqrt{12}GM + \frac{\sqrt{3}}{54}\frac{l^2}{GM} + \mathcal{O}(l^2) \, . \tag{22}$$

Finally, the correction to critical angular momentum also contains no linear terms. Furthermore, the correction decreases like $1/M$ which makes it negligible for solar system scales. As an example, black hole with solar mass has the critical angular momentum per unit mass of the order of 10^{46} $1/kg$, while obtained correction has the order of 10^{-32} $1/kg$. Moreover, correction to critical momentum ratio defines the value of instrumental accuracy, which it is desirable to have in order to measure orbital effects. For our solar system our instruments must have -74 order of precision. This value of precision lies beneath the current instruments precision.

3. Thermodynamics and PBHs

The other way to look for extended gravity experimental search is to explore black hole evaporation. Hawking showed [44] that because of quantum gravity effects, a black hole possesses a temperature. The immediate implication is that a black hole with a temperature higher than its surrounding environment evaporates. Hawking evaporation [9] is one of the most significant properties of a black hole and is described by the mass-loss rate equation as:

$$-\frac{dM}{dt} = \frac{1}{256}\frac{k_B}{\pi^3 M^2}, \tag{23}$$

where k_B is the Stefan-Boltzmann constant. In the classical physics this effect is forbidden; it appears only at a first quantization level. One of the ways to describe it is to treat that an outgoing radiation has to cross via a potential barrier of black hole horizon [47]. As a consequence an outgoing radiation surrounds a black hole. As this radiation is in a thermal equilibrium with the black hole it can be described as a black body one. A classic law for black-body radiation is:

$$-\frac{dM}{dt} = k_B S T^4, \tag{24}$$

where M is the mass of a black hole and S is its surface area. It is possible to use this formula to estimate the life-time of the black holes in the Gauss-Bonnet and Randall-Sundrum models [37]. From Eq.(23) it is obvious that for stellar masses the Hawking radiation could be neglected. This evaporation process is actual only for primordial black holes (PBH).

There is the other indirect way to observe Hawking radiation. Density fluctuations in early Universe could create PBHs with arbitrarily small masses [42, 43]. PBHs with initial masses smaller than

$$M_0 \approx 5.0 \times 10^{14} \text{ g} \tag{25}$$

are already evaporated and may contribute to the extragalactic background radiation [9]. PBHs with one greater than M_0 from Eq. (25) should evaporate just now [45]. Some models of BH evaporation predict a burst of high-energy particles at the endpoint [1, 2, 45], including gamma radiation in the MeV-TeV energy range. These events could serve as *an alternative additional* candidates for gamma ray burst (GRB) progenitors. It is necessary to point out that that any estimation for BH evaporation based on GRBs could serve only as a limit because of existing of less exotic explanations for most part of GRB events. Further, these events have radiation with very high energy and represent the most distant phenomena ($z \leq 9.4$ [46]).

Different theories give different initial PBH masses that fully evaporate during the Universe lifetime, so one can check which of them gives a result that agrees with GR. The GRB data is used because these events can be the bursts of the PBHs on the final evaporation stage [2]. The data and the precision rate of the Fermi LAT telescope [43] determine that the observable difference of the PBH initial mass on its final evaporation stage could differ from the GR predictions by 5 or more orders of magnitude:

$$\frac{M_{\text{investigated theory}}}{M_{GR}} > 10^5. \tag{26}$$

We use this limit (26) as the mass cutoff threshold.

Using the modified Parikh-Wilczek method [47, 48] (and keeping in mind its "dark side" from [49]) one rewrites the expression for the Gauss-Bonnet black hole temperature to use (6). In the astrophysical case, the dilatonic charge (see (5)) D is $\simeq 1/M$ [7] and the right hand side can be expanded as:

$$-\frac{dM}{dt} \simeq \frac{1}{256} \frac{k_B}{\pi^3 M^2} + \frac{1}{512} \frac{k_B}{\pi^3 M^6} + \mathcal{O}\left(M^{-10}\right). \tag{27}$$

hence, the initial mass of the PBH that fully evaporates during the Universe evolution is:

$$M_{\text{GB}} = 8 \times 10^{14} \text{g}. \tag{28}$$

From comparing this value with the similar GR quantity from Eq. (25) it is obvious that the obtained value is smaller than our cutoff threshold (26). Thus, at macro level there is no deviation of the Schwarzschild-Gauss-Bonnet evaporation rate from the pure Schwarzschild one. Therefore, the predictions of Gauss-Bonnet gravity for the Hawking evaporation are the same as of GR.

Now we switch to the Randall-Sundrum model solutions. The first and most studied BH solution for this theory was found by Dadhich, Maartens et al. [16, 17]. They introduced an analogy with the Reissner-Nördstrom, but instead electric charge they used a "tidal charge" q:

$$-g_{tt} = g_{rr} = 1 - \frac{2M}{r} + \left(\frac{q}{M_{p5}^2}\right)\frac{1}{r^2}, \tag{29}$$

where M_{p5} is the Planck mass in the bulk. In such a way "tidal charge" additional dimensions effects were taken into account. The mass loss rate obtained similar to the previous case is:

$$-\frac{dM}{dt} = \frac{1}{216} \frac{k_B}{\pi^3 M^2} + \mathcal{O}\left(M^{-6}\right).$$ (30)

All the difference is in the numerical coefficient in the M^{-2} order-term. It is less than the threshold parameter. The next order terms do not exist in this solution. To demonstrate this one can calculate the initial mass of the Dadhich-Rezania black hole that evaporates completely during the lifetime of the universe, using upper border value for "tidal charge" [19]:

$$M_{\mathrm{DR}} = 5.3 \times 10^{14} \mathrm{g}.$$ (31)

Eq. (31) suggests that the obtained difference is beyond the cutoff (26) so it is beyond the accuracy of current cosmological observations. Therefore, the "tidal charge" influence is negligible and cannot have experimentally verifiable consequences.

Finally, we present the calculation of the evaporation rate for the black hole of the Abdolrahimi-Page solution discussed in the previous sections. After the calculations it is seen that this solution also has no any differences from GR, i.e., its predictions coincide with the results found for the Schwarzschild BH:

$$M_{\mathrm{AP}} = 5.0 \times 10^{14} \mathrm{g}.$$ (32)

Actually, the evaporation rate of the Abdolrahimi-Page solution has completely the same form (up to M^{-10} terms) as Hawking one (23) thus, the value of the initial mass equals to that given by the GR.

Relaying on the obtained results given by Eqs. (23), (28), (30)-(32) we conclude that the precision of GRB data is not sufficient to distinguish the GR, the Gauss-Bonnet and the Randall-Sundrum gravity from each other.

4. Discussion and Conclusion

We discussed the possible ways to look for experimental tests of the theories extending GR in different ways. The Gauss-Bonnet model as the typical, but rather complex case was investigated. We also analyzed the Randall-Sundrum model with a non-compact additional dimension both in the weak and cosmological limits. For this purpose we used the PN expansion of a metric tensor and studied the PBH evaporation respectively.

The Gauss-Bonnet term does not influence the post-Newtonian limit, Eq. (7). Previously Sotiriou and Barausse [39] considered the cosmological solution of the action (3) and showed that the influence of the Gauss-Bonnet is out of the PN-order; meanwhile the contribution of the dilatonic term in the PN-expansion is negligible at solar system scales. Combination of these results, suggest that the current generation of the solar system experiments is not capable of reaching the level of sensitivity required to detect the presence of higher-order curvature corrections.

Adding the thermodynamical properties consideration claims that for the black holes with larger mass the influence of the Gauss-Bonnet term and the scalar field becomes negligibly small, therefore, the evaporation predictably is the same as in the case of GR.

The consideration of Randall and Sundrum gravity with non-compact additional dimensions [13, 14] i.e. the PN expansion of the Figueras-Wiseman solution, Eq. (10), reveals effect of a negative non-linearity of gravitational superposition. It results from the theory itself because gravity is allowed to propagate to the bulk. However, the breaking of gravitational superposition is negligibly small thus the predictions of the Randall-Sundrum theory agrees with GR and the present observations very well.

The consideration of a recent large black hole solution for RSII model of Abdolrahimi, Page et al. [35] Eq. (15), shows that the terms describing the bulk influence exceed the bounds of the 1PN approximation very far. Therefore using existing observational data, both large Randall-Sundrum black holes solutions cannot be distinguished from the Schwarzschild metric at the solar system scales.

We examined the evaporation rate in brane-world scenario as well. One of the first Randall-Sundrum BH solutions obtained by Dadhich, Maartens et al. [16] and the latest one by Abdolrahimi, Page et al. [35] (Eqs. (23), (28), (30)-(32)) were presented. The difference between the Dadhich model and the GR is negligibly small and the Page solution coincides with GR completely. Furthermore, it is easy to see that the most of the extended gravity models cannot be distinguished from GR and each other neither at the solar system scales nor by the black holes thermodynamic properties. Therefore, the coincidence of these extended theories of gravity with the GR serves a good argument in favor of their validity. However, it does not mean that no difference can be found by other verification methods. Except the weak field and the cosmological tests, a strong field approximation is widely used.

Acknowledgments

The work was supported by Federal Agency on Science and Innovations of Russian Federation, state contract 02.740.11.0575. S.A. and B.L. also were supported by individual grants from Dmitry Zimin Foundation "Dynasty". Authors would like to thank Profs. S. Capozziello and S. Turyshev for useful discussions on the subject of this work.

References

[1] S.O. Alexeyev and M.V. Pomazanov, *Phys. Rev.* D55, 2110 (1997); S.O. Alexeyev and M.V. Sazhin, *Gen. Relativ. Grav.* 8, 1187 (1998); S.O. Alexeyev, A. Barrau and K.A. Rannu, *Phys. Rev.* D79, 067503 (2009); S.O. Alexeyev and K.A. Rannu, *JETP* 114, 406 (2012).

[2] S. Alexeyev, A. Barrau, G. Boudoul, O. Khovanskaya and M. Sazhin, *Class. Quant. Grav.* 19, 4431 (2002).

[3] B. Zwiebach, *Phys. Lett.* 156B, 315 (1985); E. Poisson, *Class. Quant. Grav.* 8, 639 (1991); D. Witt, *Phys.Rev.* D38, 3000 (1988); J.T. Wheeler, *Nucl.Phys.* B268, 737

(1986), *Nucl.Phys.* B273, 732 (1986); T. Torii, H. Yajima and K. Maeda, *Phys. Rev.* D55, 739 (1997).

[4] G.W. Gibbons, K. Maeda, *Nucl. Phys.* B298, 741 (1988); D. Garfincle, G. Horowitz and A. Strominger, *Phys. Rev.* D43, 3140 (1991), *Phys. Rev.* D45, 3888 (1992).

[5] B.A. Campbell, M.J. Duncan, N. Kaloper and K.A. Olive, *Phys. Lett.* B43, 34 (1990).

[6] A. Shapere, S. Trivedi and F. Wilczek, *Mod. Phys. Lett.* A6, 2677 (1991).

[7] S. Mignemi, N.R. Stewart, *Phys. Rev.* D47, 5259 (1993).

[8] P. Kanti, N.E. Mavromatos, J. Rizos, K. Tamvakis, and E. Winstanley, *Phys. Rev.* D54, 5049 (1996), *Phys. Rev.* D57, 6255 (1998).

[9] V.P. Frolov and I.D. Novikov, *"Black Hole Physics: Basic Concepts and New Developments"* (Kluwer Academic Publishers, 1997).

[10] A.A. Starobinsky, *JETP Letters*, 86, 157 (2007).

[11] S. Capozziello, M. De Laurentis, *Phys. Rept.* 509, 167 (2011).

[12] G. Dautcourt, *Gen. Rel. Grav.* 28 905 (1996); T. Chiba, *Phys. Lett.* B575, 1 (2003); T. Chiba, T.L. Smith and A.L. Erickcek, *Phys. Rev.* D75, 124014 (2007); K. Kainulainen and D. Sunhede, *Phys. Rev.* D 78, 063511 (2008); T. Multamaki and I. Vilja, *Phys. Lett.* B 659, 843 (2008); Kh. Saaidi and A. Aghamohammadi, *Astrophys. Space Sci.* 333, 327 (2011); A. de Felice and S. Tsijikawa, *Liv. Rev. Rel.* 13, 3 (2010).

[13] L. Randall and R. Sundrum, *Phys. Rev. Lett.* 83, 3370 (1999).

[14] L. Randall and R. Sundrum, *Phys. Rev. Lett.* 83, 4690 (1999).

[15] S. de Haro, K. Skenderis and S. Solodukhin, *Commun. Math. Phys.* 217, 595 (2001), *Class. Quant. Grav.* 18, 3171 (2001).

[16] N. Dadhich, R. Maartens, P. Papadopoulos and V. Rezania, *Phys. Lett.* B487, 1 (2000).

[17] R. Maartens, *Phys. Rev.* D62 084023 (2000).

[18] A. Chamblin, S.W. Hawking and H.S. Reall, *Phys. Rev.* D61, 065007 (2000); N. Dadhich, *Phys. Lett.* B492 357 (2000); T. Shiromizu and M. Shibata, *Phys. Rev.* D62 127502 (2000); S. Nojiri, O. Obregon, S.D. Odintsov and S. Ogushi, *Phys. Rev.* D62, 064017 (2000); A. Chamblin, H.S. Reall, H. Shinkai and T. Shiromizu, *Phys. Rev.* D63, 064015 (2001); L.A. Anchordoqui, H. Goldberg andA l.D. Shapere, *Phys. Rev.* D66, 024033 (2002).

[19] S.O. Alexeyev and D.A. Starodubtseva, *JETP* 111, 576 (2010).

[20] T. Tanaka, Prog. Theor. *Phys. Suppl.* 148, 307 (2002).

[21] R. Emparan, A. Fabbri and N. Kaloper, *J. High Energy Phys.* 08, 043 (2002).

[22] R. Emparan, J. Garcia-Bellido and N. Kaloper, *JHEP* 01, 079 (2003).

[23] A.L. Fitzpatrick, L. Randall and T. Wiseman, *JHEP* 11, 033 (2006).

[24] R. Gregory, S.F. Ross and R. Zegers, *JHEP* 09, 029 (2008).

[25] T. Wiseman, *Phys. Rev.* D65, 124007 (2002).

[26] T. Wiseman, *Classical Quantum Gravity* 20, 1137 (2003).

[27] H. Kudoh, T. Tanaka, and T. Nakamura, *Phys. Rev.* D68, 024035 (2003).

[28] H. Kudoh, *Prog. Theor. Phys.* 110, 1059 (2003).

[29] H. Kudoh, *Phys. Rev.* D69, 104019 (2004).

[30] H. Yoshino, *J. High Energy Phys.* 01, 068 (2009).

[31] B. Kleihaus, J. Kunz, E. Radu, and D. Senkbeil, *Phys. Rev.* D83, 104050 (2011).

[32] P. Figueras and T. Wiseman, *Phys. Rev. Lett.* 107, 081101 (2011).

[33] P. Figueras, J. Lucietti and T. Wiseman, *Class. Quant. Grav.*, 28, 215018 (2011).

[34] D.J. Kapner, T.S. Cook, E.G. Adelberger, J.H. Gundlach, B.R. Heckel, C.D. Hoyle, H.E. Swanson, *Phys. Rev. Lett.*, 98, 021101 (2007).

[35] S. Abdolrahimi, C. Cattoen, D. N. Page and S. Yaghoobpour-Tari, *JCAP* 06, 039 (2013).

[36] S.G. Turyshev, *Phys. Usp.* 52, 1 (2009).

[37] S.O. Alexeyev, K.A. Rannu, P.I. Dyadina, B.N. Latosh and S.G. Turyshev, "Observational Limits on Gauss-Bonnet and Randall-Sundrum Gravities", submitted to *Phys. Rev. D*

[38] C.M. Will *"Theory and experiment in gravitational physics"* (Cambridge Univ. Press, 1981).

[39] T. Sotiriou, E. Barausse, *Phys. Rev.* D75, 084007 (2007).

[40] R. Ruffini and J.A. Wheeler, *Physics Today* 24, 30 (1971).

[41] M. Sasaki, T. Shiromizu and K. Maeda, *Phys. Rev.* D62, 024008 (2000).

[42] B.J. Carr, K. Kohri, Y. Sendouda and J. Yokoyama, *Phys. Rev.* D81, 104019, (2010).

[43] T.U. Ukwatta, D. Stump, J.T. Linnemann et al., arXiv:astro-ph.HE/1308.4912 (2013).

[44] S. W. Hawking, *Nature* 248, 30 (1974), *Comm. Math. Phys.* 43, 199 (1975).

[45] J. H. MacGibbon and B. J. Carr, *Astrophys. J.*, 371, 447 (1991).

[46] A. Cucchiara, A.J. Levan, D.B. Fox et al., *ApJ* 736, 7 (2011).

[47] M.K. Parikh and F. Wilczek, *Phys. Rev. Lett.* 85, 5042 (2000).

[48] S. Shankaranarayanan, T. Padmanabhan and K. Srinivasan, *Class. Quant. Grav.* 19, 2671 (2002).

[49] V. Akhmedova, T. Pilling, A. deGill, D. Singleton, *Phys. Lett.* B666 269 (2008); T. Pilling, *Phys. Lett.* B660, 402 (2008).

[50] S. Chandrasekhar, *The Mathematical Theory of Black Holes*. New York: Oxford University Press (1983)

[51] T. Damour and G. Exposito-Farèse, *Phys. Rev.* D53, 5541 (1996).

[52] K.G. Arun, L. Blanchet, B.R. Iyer and M.S.S. Qusailah, *Phys. Rev.* D77, 064034 (2008); G. Faye, S. Marsat, L. Blanchet and B.R. Iyer, gr-qc/1210.2339v1 (2012); S. Marsat, A. Bohe, L. Blanchet and A. Buonanno, gr-qc/1307.6793v1 (2013).

In: Advances in Black Holes Research
Editor: Abraham Barton

ISBN: 978-1-63463-168-6
© 2015 Nova Science Publishers, Inc.

Chapter 6

GENERALISED BRANS-DICKE MODELS FROM KALUZA-KLEIN REDUCTIONS

Davood Momeni and Ratbay Myrzakulov
Eurasian International Center for Theoretical Physics,
Eurasian National University, Astana, Kazakhstan

Abstract

In this chapter we show that how a generalized Kaluza-Klein (KK) dimensional reduction of the higher dimensional $n \geq 4$ Einstein-Hilbert action exists when more than one compactified coordinate introduced. We show that if we start by a metric with q numbers of commutative Killing vectors, the result is a $(n-q)$ scalar-tensor theory in which a couple of scalar fields coupled non minimally to the gravity. Explicitly we saw the emergence of a non minimally coupled bi-scalar-tensor model for the higher dimensional classical action is natural. By starting from a curved space-time in $(D + p)$-dimensional p-static metric, we perform the successive p-time reduction, we obtain the Einstein gravity with a unique scalar field in D-dimensions.

1. Introduction

Gravity is described by a classical gauge theory [1]. At two regimes of energy, one at high energies when the Universe created and later at the late time when we live, this classical formulation needs to be modified. Two types of modifications are needed: at high energy regime the model does not respect to the Lorentz symmetry and maybe we can use a non relativistic modification [2]. But at large scale we need an effective higher order corrected model which it must have a good cosmological behaviour.

Different approach to the gravity as a classical gauge theory proposed like Brans-Dicke (BD) theory [3] , $F(R)$ [4]- [9]). The last example is based on curvature R. It is reducible to scalar-tensor by an appropriate redefinition of the auxiliary scalar field ψ. Another type of scalar field models are obtained if we adopt a specific form of metric decomposition, so called as Kaluza-Klein (KK) [10]-[14]. In KK reduction the idea is we compactified a number of extra dimensions,namely y in a circle,it means this coordinate should be $y \sim y + 2\pi L$ (L is the size of extra dimension). From a five dimensional spacetime with the fifth coordinate as the compactified coordinate,then the reduced action of gravity is proportional to a four dimensional scalar-tensor model. But the question is if we compactified more than one coordinate,and if these coordinates do not show any time,is it possible to reduce the action of gravity to a lower dimensional action of a type of scalar-tensor?. This is our main goal in this chapter. We show that a non-minimally coupled bi-scalar-tensor theory of the gravity is obtained from a type of dimensional reduction in the sense of KK.

2.   From Einstein-Hilbert Action to Non-Minimally Coupled Scalar Field

Our Lorentzian metric is denoted by $g \equiv g_{\mu\nu}(x^\alpha)$ in which the Greek indices run μ, $\nu = 0, \ldots, n$. The spatial part of the metric is denoted by the Latin indices i, j, $\cdots = 1, \ldots, n$. We assume that the space-time coordinates are defined by $x^\mu \equiv \{x^0, x^i\}$. Here x^0 denotes a type of time. The following geometric representation of the metric is observed:

$$g = g_{\mu\nu}dx^\mu \otimes dx^\nu. \tag{1}$$

We assume that the metric is static with respect to the x^0 such that:

$$\frac{\partial g_{\mu\nu}}{\partial t} = 0, \quad g_{it} = 0. \tag{2}$$

We define the following parameterization of metric of $n \geq 4$ space-time:

$$V_n: \quad g = g_{\mu\nu}dx^\mu \otimes dx^\nu = -e^{2\gamma}dt \otimes dt + e^{2\sigma}\gamma_{ij}dx^i \otimes dx^j. \tag{3}$$

Here γ_{ij} is static with respect to the x^0:

$$\frac{\partial \gamma_{ij}}{\partial x^0} = 0, \quad \gamma_{i0} = 0. \tag{4}$$

A representation of this metric is :

$$V_{n-1}: \quad dl^2 = \gamma_{ij}dx^i \otimes dx^j. \tag{5}$$

As we observe that, the lower dimensional space-time is a subset of the higher dimensional one as the following:

$$V_{n-1} \subset V_n. \tag{6}$$

A possibility exists in a such way that the subspace metric γ_{ij} be static not only with respect to the x^0 but also with respect to a set of coordinates which we denote by $X = \{x^0, x^1, ..., x^{q-1}\}$, $n - q \leq 4$. For example a five dimensional static spherically symmetric metric is static with respect to the $X = \{t, \varphi, y\}$. So, the expected reduced action is $d = 2$ dimensional. We start by the Einstein-Hilbert action in n-dimensional metric in the following form:

$$S_n = \int \frac{R_n}{2\kappa_n^2}\sqrt{-g}d^n x, \tag{7}$$

Here R_n denotes the Ricci scalar of the n-dimensional space-time. Also the n dimensional gravitational coupling is $\kappa_n^2 \equiv 8\pi G_n$. Using Eq. (3), the Ricci scalar R_n $Ricci(V_n) = R_n$ is computed at the following:

$$
\begin{aligned}
R_n &= e^{-2\sigma} \left[R_{n-1} + 2(n-2) \triangle \sigma + 2 \triangle \gamma + 2(n-3)\partial_i\sigma\partial^i\gamma \right. \\
&\left. + (n-2)(n-3)\partial_i\sigma\partial^i\sigma + 2\partial_i\gamma\partial^i\gamma \right] .
\end{aligned}
\tag{8}
$$

Indeed, there is a recursion relation for R_n and R_{n-1}. It is possible to replace R_{n-1} by a simple way in terms of R_{n-2} and by continuing it up to the R_4 we obtained the explicit form of R_n in terms of the lower order terms of the sequence of the metric functions $\{\sigma_i, \gamma_i\}$. Mathematically we can write it as the following:

$$
R_n = e^{-2\sigma_n} + f_{n,n-1},
\tag{9}
$$

We derive the formal solution for R_n:

$$
\begin{aligned}
R_n &= e^{-2\Sigma_{l=0}^{k-1}\sigma_{n-l}} R_{n-k} + f_{n,n-1} + e^{-2\sigma_n} f_{n-1,n-2} \\
&+ e^{-2(\sigma_n+\sigma_{n-1})} f_{n-2,n-3} + e^{-2(\sigma_n+\sigma_{n-1}+\sigma_{n-2})} f_{n-3,n-4} + \cdots \\
&+ e^{-2(\sigma_n+\sigma_{n-1}+\ldots+\sigma_{n-k/2})} f_{n-(k-1),n-k} + \cdots .
\end{aligned}
\tag{10}
$$

Where $k = n - 4 > 0$.

We mention here that in the above equation, all the derivatives are written with respect to V_{n-1} : $h_{ij}dx^i \otimes dx^j$ in Eq. (5), where

$$
\partial_i f = \frac{\partial f}{\partial x^i}, \quad \triangle = h^{-1/2}\partial_i(h^{ik}h^{1/2}\partial_k).
\tag{11}
$$

To have more proceed on our reduction, we need the determinant of the V_n,

$$
\sqrt{-g} = e^{\gamma+(n-1)\sigma} \sqrt{h}.
\tag{12}
$$

We assume that the coordinate x^0 is compactified :

$$
x^0 \sim x^0 + 2\pi R.
\tag{13}
$$

We re-parameterize the metric functions by the next new set of functions:

$$
\lambda = \frac{n-3}{2}\sigma, \quad \mu = \gamma + \lambda.
\tag{14}
$$

It is not so difficult to show that Eq. (7) can be written in the following form:

$$
\begin{aligned}
S_{n-1} &= \int \frac{\sqrt{h}e^{\mu+\lambda}}{2\kappa_n^2} d^{n-1}x \left[R_{n-1} + 2 \triangle \mu + \frac{2(n-1)}{n-3} \triangle \lambda \right. \\
&\left. + \frac{2(n-1)}{n-3}\partial_i\lambda\partial^i\lambda + 2\partial_i\mu\partial^i\mu \right] .
\end{aligned}
\tag{15}
$$

The action is defined on a $(n-1)$-dimensional boundary manifold ∂M, so we obtain:

$$\int \sqrt{h} e^{\mu+\lambda} \triangle \mu d^{n-1}x = \int_{\partial M} \sqrt{h} h^{ij} n_i \partial_j \mu e^{\mu+\lambda} d^{n-2}x$$
$$- \int h^{1/2} h^{ij} \partial_j \mu (\partial_i \mu + \partial_i \lambda) e^{\mu+\lambda} d^{n-1}x, \qquad (16)$$

Here n_i is the unit normal vector to the hyper surface $x^{n-1} \equiv$ constant. We proceed the reduction to find:

$$S_{n-1} = \int \sqrt{h} e^{\mu+\lambda} d^{n-1}x \left[\frac{R_{n-1}}{2\kappa_n^2} - \frac{2(n-2)}{\kappa_n^2(n-3)} \partial_i \mu \partial^i \lambda \right]$$
$$+ \kappa_n^{-2} \int_{\partial M} \sqrt{h} h^{ij} n_i e^{\mu+\lambda} d^{n-2}x \left(\partial_j \mu + \frac{n-1}{n-3} \partial_j \lambda \right), \qquad (17)$$

The second part is bounded the term on the ∂M which can not be set to zero.

Now we define a pair of the new functions Φ and Ψ by $\mu \equiv \ln \sqrt{\Phi \Psi}$ and $\lambda = \ln \sqrt{\frac{\Psi}{\Phi}}$. By plugging these functions in S_{n-1} we obtain:

$$S_{n-1} = \int \frac{\sqrt{h} d^{n-1}x}{2\kappa_n^2} \left[\Phi \left(R_{n-1} - \frac{\omega}{4} \frac{\Phi_{,i} \Phi^{,i}}{\Phi^2} \right) + \frac{\omega \Phi}{4} \frac{\Psi_{,i} \Psi^{,i}}{\Psi^2} \right], \qquad (18)$$

where

$$\omega = \frac{2(n-2)}{n-3}. \qquad (19)$$

The action (18) defines a non-minimally coupled Lagrangian of BD-type theory in with the BD parameter is identified as $\omega_{BD} = \frac{\omega}{4}$. We suppose that $2 \leq n < 3$. In the presence of a non-zero gauge field A_I with $n = D + 1$, $\sigma = \phi$, $\gamma = (D-2)\phi$ the model is nothing just KK action.

Our proposed action has the following trivial symmetries:

Diffeomorphism invariance. The Eq. (18) remains invariant under the $(n-1)$-dimensional diffeomorphism transformations:

$$x^I \to x^I + \zeta(x^k). \qquad (20)$$

It is easy to show that under this specified transformation, the metric tensor $h_{ij}(\subseteq V_{n-1})$ behaves like a rank 2 tensor.

Gauge transformations along the compactified coordinate. We also observe that the model of bi-scalar-tensor proposed by (18) is invariant under the following global gauge transformations

$$t \to t + \beta(x^k). \qquad (21)$$

We have more gauge freedoms.

Also we can show that our model reduces to the general relativity minimally coupled to a scalar field and the one proposed in KK theory.

Case (i) General relativity (GR) with a massless scalar field: is obtained when $\mu = -\lambda$:

$$S_{n-1} = \int \sqrt{h} d^{n-1}x \left(\frac{R_{n-1}}{2\kappa_n^2} + \frac{2(n-2)}{\kappa_n^2(n-3)}\mu_{,i}\mu^{,i} \right) - \frac{2\kappa_n^{-2}}{n-3} \int_{\partial M} \sqrt{h} h^{ij} n_i \mu_{,j} d^{n-2}x. \quad (22)$$

This model has an exact black hole solution [15].

Case (ii) The KK theory in the Einstein frame in the absence of the $U(1)$ gauge field: If we set $n = D + 1, \sigma = \phi, \gamma = (D-2)\phi$ we find:

$$S_{n-1} = \int d^D x \sqrt{h}\phi \left(\frac{R_D}{2\kappa_D^2} - \frac{3}{2}(D-1)(D-2)\partial_i\phi\partial^i\phi \right). \quad (23)$$

In this new model, the name of scalar field ϕ is dilaton. We suppose that S^1 exists near a point of x^μ of V_{n-1}. The metric of this case is:

$$ds^2|_{S^1} = e^{2\gamma}dt^2. \quad (24)$$

The size of the S^1 is:

$$\int_{S^1} \equiv \int_0^{2\pi R} ds_{S^1} = 2\pi Re^\gamma \quad (25)$$

We observe that the effective radius of S^1 is Re^γ.

Furthermore the equations of motion of Eq. (18) are derived as follows:

$$r_{ij} - \frac{1}{2}rh_{ij} = \frac{1}{\Phi}\frac{\zeta}{8}\frac{\omega_{BD}\Phi}{\Psi^2}\left(2\Psi_{,i}\Psi_{,j} - h_{ij}\Psi_{,k}\Psi^{,k} \right)$$
$$+ \frac{\omega_{BD}}{\Phi^2}\left(\Phi_{,i}\Phi_{,j} - \frac{1}{2}h_{ij}\Phi_{,k}\Phi^{,k} \right) + \frac{1}{\Phi}\left(\Phi_{,i,j} - h_{ij}\triangle\Phi \right), \quad (26)$$

$$\triangle\Phi = \frac{\kappa_n^2}{3+2\omega}\left[\frac{\omega_{BD}(3-n)}{2}\left(\frac{\zeta}{4}\frac{\partial_k\Psi\partial^k\Psi}{\Psi^2} + \frac{\partial_k\Phi\partial^k\Phi}{\Phi^2} \right) + (2-n)\frac{\triangle\Phi}{\Phi} \right], \quad (27)$$

$$\frac{1}{\sqrt{h}}\partial_i\left(\frac{\sqrt{h}\Phi h^{ij}\partial_j\Phi}{\Psi^2} \right) + \frac{2\Phi}{\Psi^3}\partial_i\Psi\partial^i\Psi = 0. \quad (28)$$

Here, $r_{ij} = R_{ij}(h)$.

To have a more generalized result of the reduction, we assume that the metric $g_{\mu\nu}$ be a $n = (D + p)$-dimensional space-time as:

$$V_{D+p} = \cup_{i=1}^p V_i \oplus \cup_{j=p}^{D+p} V_j, \quad (29)$$

$$ds_{D+p}^2 = g_{\mu\nu}dx^\mu \otimes dx^\nu = -\Sigma_{j=1}^p e^{2\alpha_j}dt_j \otimes dt_j$$
$$+ e^{2\Sigma_{j=1}^p \sigma_j}h_{AB}dx^A \otimes dx^B, \quad (30)$$

$$\{A, B\} = \{p, p+1, ..., p+D\}, \quad \alpha_j = 2\left(\Sigma_{l=1}^j \gamma_l + \Sigma_{l=1}^{j-1}\sigma_l \right). \quad (31)$$

$$g_{\mu,a} = 0, \quad \frac{\partial g_{\mu\nu}}{\partial x^a} = 0. \quad (32)$$

For example Bianchi-I metric in four-dimensions are $p = 3$-static in $n = D + p = 4$ or any static-spherically symmetric space-times in four-dimensions are $p = 2$-static in $n = D + p = 4$ Using Eq. (30), we reduce the action S_{p+D} to the lower D dimensional one. Furthermore we assume that the metric h_{AB} is static with respect to all the time" coordinates $X = \{t_j\}$ as the following

$$h_{A,t_j} = 0, \quad \frac{\partial h_{AB}}{\partial t_j} = 0, \quad 1 \le j \le p. \tag{33}$$

As we know that the Ricci scalar of V_{D+p} and that of V_D are related as the following:

$$R_{D+p} = R_D + 2\Gamma_{,A}\Gamma^{,A}, \quad \Gamma_{,A}\Gamma^{,A} = \Sigma_{l=1}^{p}\partial_{,A}\gamma_l\partial^{,A}\gamma_l. \tag{34}$$

Consequently we show that S_{D+p} reduced to S_D in the following form:

$$S_D = \frac{S_{D+p}}{\int \Pi_{j=1}^{p} dt_j} = \int \frac{e^{\Sigma_{j=1}^{p}\alpha_j}\sqrt{h}d^D x}{2\kappa_{D+p}^2} \left(R_D + 2\Gamma_{,A}\Gamma^{,A} \right), \tag{35}$$

We mention here that S_D is independent of the coordinates t_j with $1 \le j \le p$ where ,

$$t_j \to t_j + \beta_j(x^k), \quad 1 \le j \le p. \tag{36}$$

Or equivalently we have:

$$S_D = \int \frac{e^{\Sigma_{j=1}^{p}\alpha_j}\sqrt{h}d^D x}{2\kappa_D^2} \left(R_D + 2\Gamma_{,A}\Gamma^{,A} \right), \quad \kappa_D^2 = \frac{\kappa_{D+p}^2}{\Pi_{j=1}^{p} dt_j}. \tag{37}$$

Specially when $\Sigma_{j=1}^{p}\alpha_j = 0$, , the action of S_D is equivalent to the Einstein gravity plus the auxiliary scalar field:

$$S_D = \int \frac{\sqrt{h}d^D x}{2\kappa_D^2} \left(R_D + 2\Gamma_{,A}\Gamma^{,A} \right). \tag{38}$$

We conclude that by starting of a curved space-time in $(D + p)$-dimensional p-static, we perform the numbers of p-time reduction, finally we obtain the Einstein gravity with a unique the scalar field in D-dimensions. We mention here that recently we extended and applied this formalism to study instabilities of anti-de Sitter space-times [16].

3. Conclusion

In summary we show that the higher dimensional Einstein-Hilbert action reduces to a lower dimensional scalar-tensor theory. We use the same decomposition of the higher dimensional metric as it was used in KK theory. The main difference and motivation of our work is that we generalize it to the case with more than one compactified coordinate. These extra coordinates are compactified in a circle. We introduced the idea of p-static metrics. For a generic n-dimensional Lorentzian metric, if there exist p-numbers of commutative Killing vectors (or p-numbers of cyclic coordinates of the point like Lagrangian of a test particle in this curved background) we show that the gravitational action of n-dimensional action reduced to $(n - p)$ dimensional Einstein-scalar model. This last reduction is new and has a central key role in gravitational theory because the exact black holes existed for this last theory.

References

[1] M. Carmeli, *Classical Fields: General Relativity and Gauge Theory*, World Scientific Publishing Co Pte Ltd; 2nd Revised edition edition (2001),ISBN-10: 9810247877.

[2] P. Horava, "Quantum Gravity at a Lifshitz Point," *Phys. Rev. D* 79, 084008.

[3] C. Brans and R. H. Dicke,"Mach's principle and a relativistic theory of gravitation," *Phys. Rev.* 124, 925 (1961).

[4] S. Nojiri and S. D. Odintsov, "Unified cosmic history in modified gravity: from F(R) theory to Lorentz non-invariant models," *Phys. Rept.* 505, 59 (2011) [arXiv:1011.0544 [gr-qc]].

[5] S. Nojiri and S. D. Odintsov, "Introduction to modified gravity and gravitational alternative for dark energy," eConf C 0602061, 06 (2006) [*Int. J. Geom. Meth. Mod. Phys.* 4, 115 (2007)] [hep-th/0601213].

[6] K. Bamba and S. D. Odintsov, "*Universe acceleration in modified gravities: F(R) and F(T) cases*," arXiv:1402.7114 [hep-th].

[7] S. Capozziello and V. Faraoni, *Beyond Einstein Gravity* (Springer, 2010)

[8] S. Capozziello and M. De Laurentis, "Extended Theories of Gravity," *Phys. Rept.* 509, 167 (2011) [arXiv:1108.6266 [gr-qc]].

[9] K. Bamba, S. Capozziello, S. Nojiri and S. D. Odintsov, "Dark energy cosmology: the equivalent description via different theoretical models and cosmography tests," *Astrophys. Space Sci.* 342, 155 (2012) [arXiv:1205.3421 [gr-qc]].

[10] M. J. Duff, B. E. W. Nilsson and C. N. Pope, "Kaluza-Klein Supergravity," *Phys. Rept.* 130, 1 (1986).

[11] T. Appelquist, A. Chodos and P. G. O. Freund, *Modern Kaluza-Klein Theories* (Addison-Wesley, Reading, 1987).

[12] J. M. Overduin and P. S. Wesson, "Kaluza-Klein gravity," *Phys. Rept.* 283, 303 (1997) [gr-qc/9805018].

[13] Y. Fujii and K. Maeda, *The Scalar-Tensor Theory of Gravitation* (Cambridge University Press, Cambridge, United Kingdom, 2003).

[14] C. N. Pope, lectures on *Lectures on Kaluza-Klein theory* (2000), http://people.physics.tamu.edu/pope/ihplec.pdf.

[15] H. A. Buchdahl, "Reciprocal Static Metrics and Scalar Fields in the General Theory of Relativity," *Phys. Rev.* 115, 1325 (1959).

[16] K. Bamba, D. Momeni and R. Myrzakulov, arXiv:1404.4255 [hep-th].

INDEX

INDEX